Pioneering Physician

The life of
Charles Fletcher
1911-1995

Pioneering Physician

The life of
Charles Fletcher
1911-1995

His story as told to
Max Blythe

with a foreword by
Professor Sir Richard Peto FRS

Contents

Introduction and acknowledgements   vii – ix
Foreword   xi

1   Background   1
2   Cambridge 1930-36   9
3   Medical training years at
   St Bartholomew's Hospital 1936-39   19
4   Wartime jobs, 1939-45, marriage, diabetes
   and my part in the penicillin story   27
5   Six years in South Wales building an
   MRC Unit to unravel the scourge of
   coal miners' pneumoconiosis   65
6   The worst of times: a difficult return to
   clinical medicine, including severe depression
   and tuberculosis   113
7   Pioneering bronchitis studies, becoming
   Britain's first TV doctor and not becoming
   the professor of medicine at Bart's   123
8   Tracking the natural history of chronic bronchitis,
   promotion to a university reader's post,
   initiating postgraduate GP education on TV   145
9   The founding of ASH, becoming a professor
   at sixty, two major publications, retirement
   from the NHS in 1976   167
10   Later years, still campaigning, final analysis   185

Epilogue: Family Reminiscences   193
Endnotes   197
Index   221

Introduction
by Mark Fletcher

In the early 1980s Max Blythe approached my father with a view to producing an account of my father's life. My father agreed to work with Max and in many interviews with Max he recounted the story of his life. These interviews were recorded by Max, who has done a remarkable job of editing, compressing and re-ordering the material so as to produce a first person narrative based on the transcripts. This book is the result.

Author's note and acknowledgements

Much of this biography is in Charles Fletcher's own words. It is based on recollections recounted to me during twenty meetings in the 1980s and conclusions recorded in 1991. Additional information has been supplied by members of Charles' family and former colleagues. Literature searches and other investigations have assisted detail and accuracy. Several of Professor Fletcher's later publications covered aspects of his career, but twenty years after his death this text draws together all its stages and contributions to medicine.

1980s interviews with Mrs Louisa Fletcher, Professor Archie Cochrane, Dr John Gilson, Sir Douglas Black, the Reverend Stephan Hopkinson and Professor Fletcher's son and daughters, Mark Fletcher, Lady Susanna Lyell and Lady Caroline Clarke, provided valuable perspective, as did correspondence with Dr Cecily Tinker and comments from Lady Sheila McMichael and Sir George Godber. In recent months I have been grateful to Mark Fletcher, Lady Lyell and Lady Clarke for checking the text, valuable advisory remarks and funding the publication of this book. I am also pleased to include family recollections in an epilogue. Final thanks are to Sir Richard Peto for his sterling Foreword.

Max Blythe

ABOUT THE AUTHOR

Max Blythe began his teaching career at Charterhouse. Later he became involved in healthcare-related teaching and research at Oxford Polytechnic, then at Oxford Brookes University. He was a member of the team that planned Oxford's first degree courses in nursing and midwifery and his video-recorded interviews with leading clinicians and medical scientists became the basis of a national biographical archive at Oxford Brookes University, where he became the reader in clinical sciences in the 1990s. He is a member of Oxford's Green Templeton College and the biographer of clinical trials icon Archie Cochrane and the leading 20th century GP John Fry.

Foreword

To my delight I found that this biography of Charles Fletcher is actually an autobiography, as the author interviewed Fletcher repeatedly and has so artfully conflated the results of these recorded conversations that the entire book seems to be narrated by Fletcher, speaking in his own clear voice. Charles Fletcher was a doctor and an epidemiologist, but his most important achievements were as a great medical communicator. In the 1950s he became famous as the BBC's Television Doctor, explaining each week, with film-star good looks and charm, the mysteries of medicine to millions of viewers. Later, he helped get courses into medical curricula on improving communication to patients and, crucially, from patients. By 1960 he was probably the most famous physician in the country, resented by some who felt that the privacy of their profession was being invaded, but respected and trusted by many other doctors and by the public, and his activities in the early 1960s were at the forefront of tobacco control, first in Britain and then in many other countries.

At that time, British men had the worst death rates in the world from smoking, and Richard Doll and Bradford Hill had recently shown that in Britain, among middle-aged adults, tobacco was responsible for about half of all male deaths plus a growing proportion of all female deaths. Yet, in 1960 the hazards of smoking were properly understood by few in the medical profession and by even fewer in government, in the media, and hence in the general public. So, in Britain as elsewhere, cigarette consumption was still rising, as was lung cancer mortality. Fletcher was one of the few who understood the full magnitude of this catastrophe and, using his established reputation and communication skills (and, probably, his upper-class connections) he and George Godber persuaded the Royal

College of Physicians to produce a special report on the real hazards of smoking, of which Charles became the main author. This RCP report, a short book entitled Smoking and Health, appeared in 1962. It was extremely influential, becoming the first runaway best seller that the College had ever produced and initiating global action. In 1971 Charles produced a second RCP report on smoking, co-founded an organisation, UK Action on Smoking and Health (ASH), that has over the decades worked successfully with the media, various governments, and the general public to get appropriate action on much the biggest cause of premature death in Britain, and prepared and presented the first major report to the World Health Organisation on global tobacco hazards.

The findings of Charles Fletcher's 1962 RCP report were reinforced by the Government's Chief Medical Officer (who by then was George Godber) and by the British Medical Journal's publication of Doll and Hill's epidemiological studies of smoking and death in British doctors (showing that smoking was really serious – it didn't just kill patients, it killed doctors!), so the British medical profession as a whole rapidly accepted the health evidence. Most British doctors who still smoked gave up the habit, followed later by other professionals, then journalists, then the general population. So, over the last half century British males have had the world's best decrease in tobacco-attributed mortality — helped, of course, by the fact that in the 1960s we started with the world's worst death rates from tobacco.

Fletcher's 1962 RCP report on Smoking and Health was the first official report on this subject in any country, and when Luther Terry, the US Surgeon-General, saw it he asked President Kennedy to commission a similar report from the Surgeon-General to the US Congress. The first Surgeon-General's report on smoking appeared in 1964, was an even greater success than the RCP report, and has been followed ever since by a succession of reports on smoking from the US Surgeon-General. These reports have had substantial effects, first within the United States and then worldwide, and have prevented millions of premature deaths.

As well as unveiling the mysteries of medicine and bringing forward British and global action on smoking, Charles had an interesting family and public life which he describes concisely and readably. His father was the first head of the UK Medical Research Council, and his father-in-law was the World War I cavalry hero General Jack Seely. At Cambridge in the 1930s Charles was friendly with some notorious members of the "Apostles" who later spied for Russia, and was an oarsman in the 1933 boat race victory over Oxford. In 1941 he became the first doctor ever to administer penicillin to critically ill patients (observing its extraordinary effectiveness), diagnosed his own severe diabetes, and married Louisa in splendour in Winchester Cathedral. Dependent on insulin (and Lou) for half a century, one day while hypoglycaemic he predicted the imminent end of the world, but was calmly instructed by Lou to eat a sugar lump before this happened. He wanted good medical care for all who needed it, regardless of their ability to pay, so he was pleased by the introduction of the National Health Service in 1948 (and thereafter avoided private practice – or, when courtesy required treating an acquaintance privately, donated the fees to research). As a Medical Research Council epidemiologist in the late 1940s he worked closely with Archie Cochrane to clarify the natural history of pneumoconiosis in coal miners, substantially improving diagnostic methods and industrial practices. Crippled by depression for a few years in the early 1950s, and thereafter somewhat in the shadow of depression, his subsequent achievements and family life should inspire others similarly affected.

Care for terminally ill patients who were suffering hopelessly and wanted to die led him to the view that there were times when doctors should, despite the law, help some, though not all, to do so. In this book he describes with thoughtful compassion the first such patient he helped die, others he thought it appropriate not to help, and his help with the death of his much-loved mother after a devastating stroke.

During the 1950s he and others speculated that in smokers their chronic production of sputum with bacterial infection could be an important cause of the deterioration of their lung function that eventually led to disability or death, and to test this hypothesis he set up an epidemiological study that eventually disproved it. Characteristically, however, he welcomed the emergence of good evidence and completely accepted that his original hypothesis had been mistaken. His study did, however, show that those smokers whose lung function was deteriorating rapidly could slow the rate of further deterioration by stopping smoking, and glossy Chest Association graphs of lung function by age that illustrate his finding still grace many clinic walls in Britain.

He led many into public health and epidemiology. I collaborated with him from 1967 to 1977 on his epidemiological study of the natural history of chronic bronchitis and emphysema; we co-authored a long book on it that nobody ever read and a short paper summarising the findings (BMJ 1977; i: 1645). In the process we became good friends and I came to learn (mainly from other people, such as Richard Doll) how much Charles had achieved. Because of Charles Fletcher's achievements from the 1950s to the 1970s, many people in Britain and even larger numbers elsewhere who would otherwise have died from smoking are still alive and healthy. Charles himself died 20 years ago, but his voice and his world come vividly back to life throughout this book. I hope other readers will enjoy reading it as much as I did.

Richard Peto, University of Oxford, 2015

Chapter 1
Background

I had fortunate origins. My father was among the brightest men I have known and my mother had unforgettable elegance and kindness. Both had impressive backgrounds.

My father's father, Alfred Evans Fletcher, was an inspector of factories in Liverpool and later appointed as the chief inspector of the national alkali inspectorate set up under the Alkali Acts,[1] which brought his family to London. He had been a gold medallist in chemistry at University College London in 1851. His Yorkshire wife, Sarah, was a Morley: a cousin of philanthropist Samuel Morley MP[2] and of Prime Minister Herbert Asquith on her mother's side. My father was the sixth of their ten children, six boys and four girls, several of whom were as gifted as their parents, particularly second son Herbert and my father Walter Morley Fletcher,[3] born on 21 July, 1873.

Herbert was my father's hero. I still have a book of cuttings covering his early career. Rowing in a quarter-mile handicap race for freshmen at Cambridge he was given a fifty yards start and ended up beating the rest by almost double that distance and in the same year became a Blue. He was an impressive hurdler and quarter-miler and became president of the Cambridge University Athletics Club in 1888. His medical training took him to Bart's (St Bartholomew's Hospital Medical School, London) where he subsequently joined the staff as a physician (from 1904-1929) and eventually became a leading Harley Street specialist in children's diseases.[4]

My father followed in his brother's medical footsteps at Cambridge and similarly qualified at Bart's, but returned to Cambridge as a physiology don and fellow of Trinity

1

College. He worked with Nobel Laureate Frederick Gowland Hopkins on the relationship between lactic acid and muscle activity. Nobel laureates A V Hill (of 1922) and Edgar Adrian (of 1932), were physiology students of his. Hill's doctorate he supervised.

Father's interests were amazingly wide. He was a considerable historian, a fine self-taught keyboard player, an expert on Elizabethan playing cards, a collector of wool weights – by which wool was weighed in the 15th and 16th centuries, and a notable player of cards.

My mother's family had large paper mills in Westmorland, founded (purchased) in 1845 by her grandfather, James Cropper.[5] Her father, Charles Cropper,[6] had taken over the firm soon after she was born, in 1881, following his father's election to parliament as the MP for Kendal. She was the third of Charles's five children and grew up at Ellergreen, the family home that James had built in several delightful acres in 1848 on a hillside above his Burneside mills.

My father fell in love with Mary "Maisie" Cropper when she visited Trinity College in 1902 to attend the summer ball with her brother James ("Jem"), an undergraduate on his landing. They were married in 1904.

I joined them in 1911 (born on 5 June), two years after my sister Anne, and vaguely remember Burrel's Field,[7] the fine house in which we lived in Cambridge until the end of 1913, when my father became Secretary of the newly formed Medical Research Council (originally the Medical Research Committee) and we moved to London (living initially at 23 Bedford Gardens W8 and later at 15 Holland Street W8).

Father was amiably caring, but so often away from the house as the head of a new national research council that he registered little on my very early years. If he had died I would hardly have noticed, but if mother had then my life would have felt in ruins. She was a lovingly attentive childhood ally and first tutor, reading to us each evening, often bible stories. With her we prayed rather formally before bed. From her strongly religious Cropper background she had a deep love of God and told me on more than one occasion of hopes that I might achieve saintly status.

Before I was born she had a promising career as a singer, but early pressures of motherhood led to a tragic loss of voice at a critical time when she was about to play the role of Pamina in an Edward Dent production of *The Magic Flute* at the New Theatre, Cambridge. Just hours before curtain-up a substitute had to be found to sing the part off-stage, while she acted voicelessly on stage opposite the distinguished tenor Steuart Wilson[8] as Tamino. Her confidence never completely recovered, but the voice that I occasionally heard was quite exceptional. It was her sister, Sybil Cropper, a contralto, who went on to a professional singing career.

Bonding with my father began around the age of six when he started telling me about the human body. I remember sitting on his knee one day after tea and being told how the gut worked and where the food went. Such revelations began my fascination with biology. Soon after I went to prep school he gave me a copy of Arthur Mee's *The Engines of the Human Body*, based on lectures that Mee had given at the Royal Institution. It was my father who told my mother about the facts of life in the train on the way to their honeymoon. She, in turn, educated my sister and me about sex before we reached teenage years, at a time when few children were so informed.

My schooling began in 1917 at the Norham Place School in London where I stayed happily until 1919 when I transferred to the Manor House prep school at Horsham, Sussex, which a cousin of my father had recommended. I was never happy there. I was teased, not good at games and unpopular because I was the only boy at the school who was down for Eton and whose parents had titles. My father had just been knighted (KBE) for services to medical research during the 1914-1918 War. Also, I hated boxing and the roughhouses that arose in the dormitory.

But the teaching was thorough enough. Thanks to the efficient mathematics teaching of a master called White, who had played county cricket (for Northants), I left with a sound understanding of algebra and geometry. Another master, in auditioning me for a pantomime that he had written, discovered that I had some singing and dancing ability and cast me in the leading role and arranged for me to have tap-dancing lessons. A love of performing surfaced then.

Soon after the pantomime I taught myself to swim in the school's outdoor pool and discovered an interest in the birds and plants of the school grounds, which made life in the last two years fairly tolerable.

Eton, where I went in September 1924, was wonderfully different. I went into a house run by my godfather, Alfred Conybeare,[9] my mother's cousin, and had a study-bedroom of my own, with a fireplace in which coals were laid each day by the boys' maid for a glowing evening fire. I felt at home from the first day.

Alfred Conybeare was a popular housemaster (1909-1930) and later Lower Master, then Vice-Provost. He had pioneered evening visits to the rooms of all boys to spend a few minutes conversing with each of them. This was unique to his house when I went to Eton, but soon became common to them all and subsequently spread to other schools. As a mathematics teacher he was less impressive and did not get me over the hurdle of calculus. Possibly I just reached the extent of my competence in the subject, but had enough to pass the School Certificate Examination.

I struggled with the Classics, also, but took strongly to the sciences and coped tolerably well with other subjects. Outstanding teaching by two biologists, Weatherall and White-Thompson, drew me strongly to their subject. Weatherall was a farmer's son with a Midlands accent that attracted lots of flak from Etonians, but his teaching always inspired. White-Thompson, a son of the Bishop of Ely, taught wonderfully methodically and took immense trouble in tutoring me as I prepared for Cambridge in my last year at Eton. Sadly, soon afterwards he was killed in a climbing accident.

The headmaster, Dr Cyril Alington, was a marvellous character who gave beautiful sermons; five minute talks, brilliantly constructed, each with a moral theme. As a chorister in the Junior Chapel choir I sang one or two solos, and remember particularly Handel's "Let the Bright Seraphim". Later, with the senior choir I learnt the bass parts of the psalter. Pure bliss is how I found singing in a Chapel of such magnificent architecture.

Also at Eton I began to enjoy sport; mainly on the river. I was never good at kicking or hitting a ball, but in rowing had early success and began training hard. In my last year this paid off with a place in the Eton Eight. I also became captain of house and was elected to the school society of prefects known as Pop. This was a first real experience of achievement and my father was delighted as never before.

At that stage, I began feeling his strength of support and pride in my progress. I remember telling a housemaster who was chiding me for wanting to be a scientist "like Hilliard", the least impressive science master, that my intention was to follow in the footsteps of my father who was then a fellow of the Royal Society. [3]

Half way through my first year in the sixth form, I told my father that I intended going to Cambridge to read natural sciences, with hopes of a career in medicine or medical science. On his recommendation I prepared for and took the 1st MB (Bachelor of Medicine) examination before leaving school. White-Thompson gave me the extra tuition needed for this due to the massive differences between Higher School Certificate and 1st MB requirements. This doubled my workload, but a year later (in 1929) I passed the 1st MB examinations at Cambridge, staying at my father's college, Trinity, while taking them and falling in love with the place.

My good fortune at Eton included having a second godfather there as Provost (the resident Chairman of governors). Monty James,[10] the medievalist and superb writer of ghost stories kept a close eye on my progress throughout these years, and consequently so did many of the senior staff. Monty James had been my father's closest friend at Cambridge, where he had been Provost of King's. I have been blessed with good connections.

And in my last two years at Eton I formed the first close friendships of my career: with David McKenna,[11] Bernard Fergusson,[12] and Harry Cumming-Bruce.[13]

When I went up to Cambridge and Trinity College in October 1930 my father was away in Philadelphia receiving an honorary degree, but soon after his return he visited me. I have a golden memory of walking with him from my lodgings to College, walking in through the great gate with the bell for Hall sounding and him saying "One day, that bell will mean as much to you as it does to me". I cry at the thought of that moment.... His colossal encouragement to me in school years had brought us very close and his love of Trinity College I soon shared. When I revisit nowadays as a guest of my friend Alan Hodgkin,[14] now the Master of Trinity, I feel blissfully at one with the place.

Before I talk of undergraduate years at Cambridge, my mother merits special mention for her admirable support throughout my school years, in which she wrote lovingly long letters each week and managed blissful family vacations when terms ended, many at her family home, Ellergreen, in Westmorland (now Cumbria) where I had a first taste of field sports with Cropper relations. Influenced by her deeply religious convictions I had become strongly Christian. My sister Anne and I were both deeply religious in our teenage years.

I was a rather virtuous chap when I went up to Cambridge.

Before then I spent most of the summer vacation in Munich learning German. I emerged with a useful knowledge of the language but not proficient in reading German texts, which was a disappointment when I later tried reading research documents in the language. An outstanding performance of *Die Meistersinger von Nürnberg* by the Munich Opera is my main memory of these weeks, particularly the ecstasy of Eva's entry in scene 4 of the final Act. These were days before Hitler came to power, but there were brown shirts on the streets.

*Dr Walter Morley Fletcher in 1904, the
year of his marriage to Mary "Maisie" Cropper*

Mary "Maisie" Cropper, 1904

7

Chapter 2
Cambridge 1930-36

When I went up to Cambridge my father gave wise advice that I have often handed on to undergraduates: that term-time should be mainly for enjoying university life and meeting people and that vacations were for extensive reading and revision. He also advised me to avoid mixing mainly with fellow medical students as I would be working with doctors for the rest of my life, although at Cambridge I did not become a medical student until third year because I had completed my 1stMB examinations before going up.

Initially, I read physiology, zoology and chemistry, but was never good at chemistry. Quite early in year one a chemistry tutor told me that I would be pulled down in end-of-year examinations by the chemistry papers, but I struggled to improve and with some surprise managed a First Class in Mays.

Quite early at Cambridge I became caught up in rowing, amateur dramatics and singing with the Trinity College and Cambridge Madrigal Societies in which one of my Eton friends, David McKenna, also sang. He was an engineering scholar at Trinity, with a fine tenor voice, and became my closest friend of Cambridge years. My own modestly good baritone voice had begun emerging at Eton where I sang in the senior choir in School Chapel, the magnificent perpendicular chapel built by Henry VI.

I also became caught up in the Trinity Luncheon Club and Shakespeare Society. To ensure scintillating conversation, only scholarly types were elected to the former.

The speed with which I was drawn into rowing at Cambridge was astounding. I had gone up hoping to become a hurdler like Uncle Herbert and my father, who were hurdling Blues. Although I had rowed successfully at Eton, I preferred track events and had won the senior hurdles before leaving. But I had not accounted for the pressure that would be put on me by my father and the Third Trinity Boat Club,[1] then the most successful college rowing club in Cambridge, which had won the light-fours in six successive years and wanted me to help make it seven. Being asked to take part was difficult to resist and I found myself put into the boat with three Blues in front of me and winning the race easily. A day later I was invited to join the Boat Race squad. It all happened that fast. Although I turned down the invitation and did not row in trial eights, with intentions still of becoming a track athlete, I had a second invitation during the Christmas vacation, which my father persuaded me to accept. A letter from Tom Brocklebank, who was then stroking the Cambridge crew and president of the Cambridge University Boat Club, asked me to reconsider and return for training before term began in January, 1931. This, my father urged me to do to be certain of getting a Blue, which he considered of far greater importance than I ever did. He regarded my chances of a hurdling Blue as too uncertain and advised me to concentrate on rowing, but being good at something that I did not enjoy seemed unfortunate.

Long daily training sessions on the river became the dominating aspect of my second term, before the end of which the Boat Race crew went off to Goring-on-Thames in Oxfordshire for intense final preparations. There, bad luck struck and a whitlow (a swollen infected finger) impeded my rowing badly enough to lose me my place in the boat. On my last grim day of training, a week before the Race, I almost collapsed before we had completed a mile and needed an operation to relieve the swelling. So, staphylococcal septicaemia ended my first shot at a Blue; a bitter experience because I had invested many hours in training and given up many things I would have preferred doing. At the time of being dropped from the crew I could have been in Sweden with the Trinity College Madrigal Society.

But I sang with the Trinity College and Cambridge Madrigal Societies in the summer term, also in a little-known operetta that students put on in May Week. David McKenna had the principal tenor role and my sister Anne the soprano lead. She was studying at the Webber Douglas School of Singing in London, but leapt at the chance of singing with us in Cambridge. I had a minor role, playing a cockney character, but took to the necessary accent with surprising ease. All my mother's family were excellent raconteurs, good at conjuring up accents and it was good discovering that I had a little of their flair.

I went up to Cambridge early that summer to have special lectures from Joseph Barcroft,[2] the professor of physiology, whose teaching I had missed while at Goring with the Boat Race crew. With typical kindness he had offered me and Charles Sergel, another medical student in the crew (later president of the Cambridge University Boat Club), this opportunity to cover the physiology that we had missed. Barcroft was a wonderfully amiable man,

Charles Fletcher, Cambridge University oarsman, 1931

11

whose research on haemoglobin and the oxygenation of blood had taken him to the tops of mountains. At this time he was investigating foetal respiration. His research later earned him a knighthood.

In my second year at Cambridge I did not row for two terms due to a series of streptococcal infections that followed the original whitlow infection. Consequently, I read more and had the advantage of this when I took my BA degree in May 1932 in natural sciences (physiology, zoology and chemistry), when I got a first and had the surprise satisfaction of being awarded a senior scholarship at Trinity. One of my physiology examiners, Dr Neville Willmer (later FRS),[3] whom I later knew quite well, confided in me that I had made impressive use of limited knowledge. I think this sums-up much that I have done in my career. It has been a story of making good use of fairly average memory banks. I have always had a sense of inferiority alongside scholarly medical colleagues brimming with knowledge.

Summer vacations in these Cambridge years were typically spent in Westmorland at my mother's family home, Ellergreen, or with relations in the West Country, often at Killerton,[4] an estate belonging to my uncle Francis Acland[5] who had married my mother's eldest sister, Eleanor Margaret. Like my father, I greatly enjoyed the country estate life, especially such outdoor activities as shooting. But I always felt bad about killing. Golf I was never good at, but played during holidays hoping to improve. One or two holidays with the Aclands were in Donegal where they used to go in summer to Marble Hill (on the North West coast of the County). On one of these breaks I hired a bike and went off alone exploring the Donegal coast and discovering its beauty.

In my third year at Cambridge I prepared for the 2nd MB examination and, free of streptococcal infection, regained a place in the Cambridge boat race crew. Also, I became secretary of the Pitt Club, a club for undergraduates, almost a junior version of a London gentlemen's club, dating from 1835 and of which my father was writing a history.[6] During his visits to Cambridge to research this we often took long afternoon walks together on which our friendship considerably advanced, with him sometimes tutoring me brilliantly. On one occasion when I was struggling to understand some aspect of parathyroid functioning he simply and entertainingly put it all succinctly into perspective. Until then, I had never quite appreciated how remarkable he was.

His sudden death soon afterwards (on 7 June 1933, aged 59) left me starkly bereft. He had gone through several illnesses in the last few years and so it was not entirely a shock, but coming to terms with the loss took several years in which I felt robbed of a treasured adviser and the deepest relationship I had known.

Almost sixty years later there are still occasions when I want to turn to him for advice. If he had lived, then many of the mistakes made in my early career would have been averted by his wisdom.

I am glad that he lived long enough to see me row in a winning Boat Race crew and become a senior scholar of Trinity, which in his last months brought him as much satisfaction as my rowing Blue. He could not have been happier than when the Cambridge crew triumphed in 1933, but Cambridge always won in those years (1924-1936).

His death at the age of 59 was due to cerebral infection that followed successful chest surgery at the Brompton Hospital by Arthur Tudor Edwards, a pioneering chest surgeon. If there had been antibiotics he would have survived. He had had various chest problems since 1918, when he had suffered near-fatal streptothrix pneumonia.[7] Three years later he had been operated on for its residual effects. A more recent health problem had been a period of confusion and memory loss in 1932 when on occasions he had not known who he was. This was not diagnosed before he made a complete recovery, but during the two or three months of the curious illness there were embarrassing reports of him being seen in Harley Street

Sir Walter Morley Fletcher FRS, c1930

wobbling about in what appeared to be a drunken haze. This did little for his position as the chief administrator of the Medical Research Council, which had already run into undermining internal politics. His last couple of years there were particularly difficult ones.

A week before his last operation he had been taken by my mother to a retreat weekend at Chichester, but had not joined in the spirit of it. He lacked her religious conviction and spent long hours meditatively alone in the quiet of the Cathedral. The faith of his early years was largely gone. He had been brought up keenly evangelical, but in teenage years had found the pious zeal of some of his parents' religious friends intolerable. At Cambridge he had attended college services and become an Anglican, but found belief difficult and dogma disturbing. He could never understand why Christ came into the world too late and left it all too soon.

Soon after his death I was drawn deeply into religion, with my mother becoming a devoted member of the Oxford Group, a religious movement popular with the upper middle classes and so called because of its high initial membership of Oxford dons. It had been founded in the 1920s by an American, Frank Buchman, a revolutionary Lutheran pastor intent on changing the spiritual conscience of the world, beginning with the influential, well-to-do classes. His Oxford Group movement preached a four-point gospel of absolute honesty, absolute purity, absolute unselfishness and absolute love and devotion to God. A few years later (in 1938) it became the Moral Rearmament Movement, of which my mother became a prominent member. Soon after her Oxford Group conversion in 1933, I also became hooked on the Movement's ideals of fervently seeking to do good and influence others.

I remained at Cambridge after my father's death, choosing not to go into medical training right away, although I had completed my 2nd MB by then. Instead I spent a fourth year (1933-34) doing part 2 physiology in the hope of following in his footsteps and becoming a research student, then a physiology tutor. Trying to emulate his achievements seemed the best way of honouring his memory. Ultimately, I hoped for a fellowship at Trinity. I largely gave up rowing, except in May Week and preparation for that, and did well enough in part 2 physiology to be awarded a Coutts Trotter and Michael Foster Scholarship. Among my best memories of Year 4 is playing the role of Box in a College production of Gilbert and Sullivan's *Box and Cox*, a part both musical and comical and increasing my love of acting that had been there since prep school days.

In year five I began physiological research investigating curious retractor muscle responses in the common mussel, *Mytilus edulis*, to which my attention had been drawn by the distinguished physiology don Frank Winton, a leading investigator of kidney functioning and co-author of the leading textbook on human physiology.[8] There was great interest in the Cambridge physiology laboratory at that time in unravelling the secrets of muscle and neurone functioning. Electrophysiology had opened the way to great revelations and I was tempted by the fascinating opportunities of this field, very wrongly as it turned out. I was not of the calibre of Cambridge's ground-breaking electrophysiologists like Adrian (later professor and Lord) and Matthews, (later professor). I lacked their research strengths in biophysics.

But I worked for about 18 months on the curious responses of isolated, live *Mytilus edulis* retractor muscle to electrical stimulation, recording patterns of contraction as stylus tracings on a revolving, smoked kymograph cylinder. It sounds antiquated now, but was the best approach then. The main findings were that a short application of direct current results in a very slow action potential and contraction, but with continued stimulation the muscle eventually contracts tightly. More fascinating, however, was the swift relaxation of the muscle when given a short shock of alternating current. My attempts at unravelling the puzzle of this were eventually reported in the *Journal of Physiology* in 1937 (3 papers). I also wrote a dissertation on the work that I hoped would earn me a junior fellowship at Trinity. I deeply wanted to be a don there, as my father had been.

But fate was not on my side. The fellowship for which I applied at Trinity in 1936 went to a brilliant junior in the physiology department, Alan Hodgkin, later a Nobel laureate, who at the last minute had been advised by his tutor Francis Roughton to put in an application, just for practice. His last-minute thesis was far better than mine, it turned out, but there was little comfort in being told that under normal circumstances mine would have gained me a fellowship. Only later did I appreciate the favour Alan Hodgkin had done me in shattering my hopes of a research career at Cambridge, in which I would have been second-rate at best. The disappointment switched me back onto medical tracks from which I should not have departed and within days I was arranging to begin medical training in the autumn of 1936.

A special memory of the Cambridge physiology department is of visiting Edgar Adrian's room and being asked "Would you like to hear a grasshopper seeing a light?" He had a grasshopper's optic nerve with electrodes on it and when he shone a light on the eye there was a resulting whirr from his apparatus as the action potential went down the nerve.

I did turn down an offer of a fellowship at Peterhouse in my fifth year, where they were looking for someone to tutor medical students. I just couldn't contemplate being a tutor anywhere other than at Trinity.

It was in that year that my evangelising as a member of the Oxford Group lost its appeal. For more than a year I had been attending Oxford Group house meetings with my mother and feeling spiritually close to her, which had been a comfort after my father's death. And my religious zeal stretched into university life where I tried enthusing colleagues with the Group's teaching. But in fifth year my enthusiasm was blunted. Feeling guided by God I had gone to see an undergraduate student of another college who seemed in deep need of moral support, but found that I had wasted my time. He was not there and I had been rain soaked on the way and lost valuable laboratory time. I felt that God could have better directed me. While I remained a strongly committed Christian my crusading began declining from that point. Only later in life did I lose faith and find greater comfort in agnostic philosophy. My sister Anne lost her faith rather early in life, but married a clergyman and had it restored.

My six years at Cambridge were rather cloistered ones. I did not have girl friends[9] and mainly spent leisure times with a small circle of friends, although in a slightly wider circle of contacts I got to know Guy Burgess and Anthony Blunt fairly well. Both were at Trinity in my time there: both becoming junior fellows in 1932. We lunched together fairly often and they frequently challenged my views on homosexuality and chided my virtuousness. Both were leading members of the Cambridge Apostles secret debating society, to which I was neither inclined nor invited. Both were already deeply communist and, as we all learned much later, eventually involved in Soviet espionage.

I remember Cambridge mainly for music and friendships. There is a particularly memorable concert given by the Cambridge Madrigal Society[10] close to the end of each summer term when members sing on a raft on the river, near to the bridge at King's College, and finally float off into the night to the sounds of "Draw on sweet night".[11] Singing on these occasions had rare delight.

A final bright recollection of this undergraduate period is rowing in the Cambridge Boat Race crew. I had never enjoyed rowing until then, but rowing with a superbly athletic and finely tuned crew was a marvellous aesthetic experience. Our performance in the actual Boat Race was not as good, due to the loss of our best oarsman (at No6) just a few days before. He had developed cholecystitis and been replaced, but we still beat Oxford comfortably by two lengths, after remaining neck-and-neck until Hammersmith. Training in winter had been tough, with cold baths obligatory each morning and out on the river our hands freezing to the oars on one occasion. But there were splendid pre-race weeks rowing at Goring-on-Thames where we stayed in a fine country house before moving on to the Hurlingham Club at Fulham and training on the Boat Race course. As Cambridge oarsmen we all became members of the Leander Club at Henley-on-Thames, where for several years I took part in Royal Regatta Week.

Chapter 3
Medical Training Years at St Bartholomew's Hospital, 1936-39

Three years before medical training I experienced the kind of satisfaction to be found in medicine. This was during a climbing holiday with four university friends in Westmorland at Easter 1933. We were out climbing on Sca Fell when the best climber of the group attempted to scale a severe rock face and fell about thirty feet onto his face. As the only colleague with medical knowledge I was pitched into deciding how to care for a badly wounded and unconscious friend. Urgently, I sent off two of the party to alert the local hospital and bring back a stretcher. Then on this bitterly cold day I concentrated on keeping the unconscious body warm, which the remaining two of us managed by lying close enough to share our body heat, then with snow beginning to fall we used a groundsheet to form a shelter. Fortunately, all went well and we got our casualty down to the hospital, where he made a full recovery.[1]

I began medical training at Bart's (St Bartholomew's Hospital London) in September, 1936. Originally, I had intended going to University College Hospital Medical School, but soon after my father's death I had been contacted by the Dean of Bart's (Dr William Girling Ball[2]) saying that I would be given free medical training if I decided to train there. In memory of my father who had trained there all fees would be waived. Not wanting to put a further burden on my mother's finances, after two rather unproductive years at Cambridge, I took up this generous offer. So, I veered from going to UCH, which had the finest array of tutors, six or seven of them fellows of the Royal Society.

But Bart's was never a disappointment and I worked on the firms of a number of distinguished clinicians. Particularly, I enjoyed contact with patients and becoming caught up in their care, on every aspect of which I made detailed notes. Talking with them about lives very different from my own did a lot for my social perspective. Similarly, I became absorbed in the applied clinical science of the time. As a ward clerk, I attended every additional clinic and ward round that fitted into off-duty moments. I made copious notes in minute writing in a small pocket book that I always had with me.

I became an avid accumulator of facts, assisted by a particularly good method of learning advocated by one of the zoology demonstrators at Cambridge. This required nightly logging of all the main facts acquired each day from lectures and clinical experience, then reading these notes a day later, then a week later, and finally a month later, to fix the data in memory. I even prepared concise sets of notes on cards; packs of cards that I could look through while travelling to Bart's each day on the underground[3] and on return journeys home (which was at 158 Hamilton Terrace. Maida Vale, NW8, where I lived with my mother). I stuck to these learning methods throughout medical training. The revision cards that I wrote were in question and answer format, with questions on one side and answers on the other. When I remembered the right answer I would tick it, and when there were three ticks would regard this knowledge as fixed.

At medical school most of the students of my year were younger and less experienced. My initial friendships were with the only two who had university degrees: David Morse (who became a surgeon at Newcastle) and Dick Cohen (who had a distinguished career at the Ministry of Health and DHSS, becoming Chief Scientist). Later, Lionel Grunbaum, a sparklingly bright young first year student, became the third close friend. Tragically his career would be cut short by polio in 1945.

Quite early on we formed an action group hoping to secure a greater say in our medical education, aspects of which we considered unhelpful, even antiquated. On these issues I spoke at a meeting of the medical students' club, suggesting that we campaign for change, but the response was poor. Most first year colleagues were as reluctant to suggest change as they would have been to suggest it to the headmaster at school. A number of them had become medical students as young as sixteen, which was possible then, and lacked reasonable maturity.

Medical education at Bart's was typical of the time, with heavy emphasis on the development of clinical knowledge and skills, but appallingly little attention to interpersonal skills with patients. Essentially we were well informed on how to treat diseases, but not the humans suffering them. This I lamented. There was a tendency for doctors to talk down to patients because of class differences or the patient's lack of biological knowledge. Keenly aware of how my father had been able to instruct me on biological matters at an early age, I felt that they were entitled to the same kind of explanation of what was happening to them and how their treatment was expected to work. It seemed an essential courtesy, but the concept of the informed patient had not dawned. Very early on I committed myself to doing the best I could to keep them in the picture, although some tutors questioned the relevance of doing so.

I had a degree of odd-man-out status in these years, being considerably older than most of my contemporaries, having the prestige of Boat Race success and being a member of a different social set to almost all other colleagues except Dick Cohen, who had a similar background. I began being invited regularly to events in the Season, mainly through Eton connections. Immaculately attired in white tie and tailcoat, looking every inch a Fred Astaire, I went to a ball almost every evening, meeting many of the glamorous debutantes being presented at Court. Being in unexpected high demand considerably raised my social confidence. Being a good dancer was a considerable asset.

There was one occasion when I attended a ball shockingly attired because I had lost the key to the cupboard in which I hung my tailcoat. The family giving the party had recommended (on the telephone) that I go in fancy dress instead. So I donned lederhosen that I had acquired in Germany. With everyone else in conventional white tie and tails I was the odd man out, but blissfully unconcerned.

I had friendships with a number of beautiful young women in these medical school years, none more engaging than with Mary Peel whom I might possibly have gone on to marry. But tragically she committed suicide, shooting herself with a shotgun. Her loss hurt and I buried myself deeply in clinical studies for several weeks.

At Bart's I used my camera to record aspects of hospital life with a humorous candid camera slant for publication in the medical school gazette. I was an early candid camera enthusiast. The published shots with their comic captions became a popular addition to the gazette, but occasionally the humour did not transmit. One photograph, taken in the autopsy room and captioned "Lighten our Darkness: a snap taken at an Oxford Group rally" brought stern criticism from a rather religious Bart's anaesthetist (Langton Hewer) who protested that religious gatherings should not be exposed to such ridicule!

The main criticism that I ran into while at Bart's was for my leftish political views, which lots of colleagues found objectionable. I was also criticised by a few close friends, particularly Lionel Grunbaum, for being too self-centred. Until then I had not been aware of this fault of thinking too much about me and having too little interest in those I was close to. I was rather self-centred and at times could be morosely preoccupied by thoughts that I would not reach my thirtieth birthday, possibly because of the number of deaths that I saw while a student. I seemed surrounded by infection risks and one or two of my student colleagues were lost to them. But as most medical students do, I developed a mental carapace shutting out anxiety for sad cases encountered on the wards.

I was never intensely political, but at Cambridge had developed socialist views. In the 1935 general election I had voted Labour, caught up in the idea of a fairer society. Soon after arriving at Bart's I had joined the London Medical Students Socialist Society. I had begun seeing enough of the problems of poverty among patients and their families to feel a committed socialist. In my second year at Bart's (1938) I took part in a debate vigorously supporting the idea of a national health service and was called "a bloody communist" by one of my student colleagues for such socialist views. But at a party later that evening, a Cambridge friend and Communist Party member accused me of being a true blue Tory. So, I was called a communist and a true blue Tory on the same day. I suspect that my privileged lifestyle and political philosophy were too confusingly ill-matched.

For my third year at Bart's I was awarded the medical school's Henry Brackenbury scholarship for medicine, and turned down the one for surgery. I had won both, but could receive only one. I was not long in deciding which to accept. I wanted to be a physician, not a surgeon. I never had interests in a surgical career, but must have done well on surgical firms as I later received an invitation (on qualifying) to be house officer to the senior surgeon, Harold Wilson,[4] which was a considerable compliment. When I turned this down, he mildly questioned my judgement by pointing out that surgeons have more directly curative roles than physicians, who are more impressive diagnostically but lack therapeutic effectiveness against many of the conditions they treated. There was a fair degree of truth in what he said. The number of diseases that could be treated satisfactorily on medical wards was limited, sometimes depressingly so. But we could treat diabetes mellitus, Addison's disease had recently become treatable and by the later 1930s sulphonamides had begun vastly increasing our effectiveness against streptococcal infections and the

23

pneumonias. I remember seeing the amazing effects of Prontosil,[5] the first sulpha-drug (the first antibiotic) on conditions that would normally have been fatal. But mainly I was able to tell Wilson that I had always felt temperamentally inclined to medicine.

My grimmest recollections of 1939, the year in which I prepared for finals, are of war with Germany looking increasingly likely. For too long most of my generation had believed that another world war could never happen and so we were largely unprepared for what had begun unfolding rapidly, with air raid shelters being urgently distributed to homes early that year and conscription introduced in the Spring, just as I took the Conjoint Board Examination. Sinister war clouds were gathering, yet British optimism made many people feel that they would somehow be dispersed. I hoped, but doubted, that they were right.

I took the Conjoint Examination (for the English Conjoint Diploma of the Royal Colleges of Physicians and Surgeons, the most basic of medical qualifications: MRCS LRCP[6]) in April and the Cambridge MB examination in May, 1939, and qualified with impressive marks. I tended to do well in examinations. I remember at Cambridge the Regius Professor of Physic, John Ryle, reading out the results and later congratulating me on exceptionally high marks.

A few days after qualifying I had the surprise offer of a travelling fellowship from the Secretary of the Medical Research Council, my father's successor Sir Edward Mellanby. The fellow appointed would undertake research into physical fitness and travel internationally for the National Fitness Council seeking the best ways of achieving it. This was all tied to military interests at a time of growing international tension, with leaders of the Armed forces concerned about the fitness of recruits. The pathetic state of Britain's youth in World War 1 had not been forgotten.

With a high salary of £600 the fellowship was tempting, but after consulting Professor T R Elliott[7] at

University College Hospital, who had become a kindly mentor after my father's death, I turned it down. Elliott pointed out that such a step was likely to end my clinical career and land me on a public health service pathway. The prospect of becoming a civil servant was not attractive.

Before returning to Bart's for my first house job at the beginning of August, I enjoyed a July motoring holiday in France with Martin Wright,[8] a Trinity man who had qualified a year ahead of me and become my closest friend at Bart's. Originally, we intended driving down to the Mediterranean coast and spending time at Nice and Monte Carlo, but with Martin's aged car playing up too frequently our plans reshaped and we toured Normandy and Brittany instead, but not without further breakdowns. Only with Martin's innovative roadside repair skills did we complete the reduced route to Rouen, Chartres, Le Mans, Lavel, Rennes, St. Brieuc and Morlaix. Later his skills as an inventor would produce the peak flow meter for respiratory medicine and one of the earliest breathalysers.

Among the happiest memories of medical school years are recollections of the theatrical events in which I took part, particularly the students' Christmas pantomimes in which I had leading parts. I greatly enjoyed acting and developing a range of accents, which I have gone on doing all my life. If I had not gone into medicine then the stage would have been my second choice of career. Fred Astaire and Jack Hulbert were great heroes.

During medical school years my mother regularly arranged musical evenings when we entertained groups of friends and sang around the piano. She was a fine accompanist and directed us impressively from the keyboard through Mozart operas, in which I sang some of the baritone arias, and Bach cantatas. She was still a wonderfully doting mother, although I had not lived up to her high expectations of becoming influentially religious. That I had not become a leading Christian evangelist was a great disappointment that she did not disguise. At 27 I was committed instead to a medical career.

I had just begun my first house job at Bart's[9] when the world was plunged into war.

Additional recollections of these Bart's years are of flirting briefly with the idea of becoming a psychiatrist, playing leading roles in productions of the Bart's Amateur Dramatics Society (in *Youth at the Helm* in Year 1 and a Galsworthy play in Year 2) and beginning noting all the jokes and humorous stories that I heard. I have gone on jotting them down for many years and using them in talks and speeches that I give.

Chapter 4
Wartime Jobs, 1939-45, marriage, diabetes and my part in the penicillin story

I was lying in a hospital bed when war was declared on 3rd September 1939. After completing my first month as a house officer at Bart's I had developed severe sinusitis and become an inpatient there. That was at the end of August. Then on the 2nd September I was transferred to a hospital at St. Alban's to which most of Bart's inpatients had already been transferred. With heavy air-raid bombing of London anticipated, central hospitals were being urgently cleared of patients. I was in the last group to leave an eerily empty Bart's.

All hospitals in London and the Home Counties had become part of a wartime Emergency Medical Service, which divided this large region into ten administrative sectors, like sectors on a pie chart, each radiating out from one or two London teaching hospitals. Bart's and the Royal Free Hospital were the teaching hospitals in Sector 3 that radiated out into Hertfordshire. At the start of the war the basic plan was for the evacuation of patients and staff of teaching hospitals to large selected hospitals on the outskirts of each sector. These sector hospitals had been preparing for this. The main role of the teaching hospitals was to serve as central emergency treatment and clearing centres, mainly for the large numbers of bombing casualties that were anticipated.

I spent the first three weeks of the war at the Hill End Hospital, St. Alban's, one of the two sector hospitals to which Bart's staff and patients had transferred. Bedford Russell,[1] the ENT specialist in charge of my treatment, washed out the sinuses in various ways without lasting benefit and finally undertook antrostomy under a general anaesthetic to broaden the sinus drainage apertures, but with disappointing results. The best moments were when the pain lessened and I lazed on a balcony on warm afternoons. I also had pleasure in watching the recovery of a young boy who had a heavily diseased lung removed; one of the earliest pneumonectomies on a child, performed by a surgeon called Roberts (possibly James Roberts). Bedford Russell being transferred back to Bart's was a blow, but on the first day that I felt well enough I was driven by my friend and fellow Bart's house physician Martin Wright to Harley Street to check on what more Russell could advise to speed my recovery. Remarkably, he advised spending a few weeks at an altitude of 600 feet or more. With friends, the Fothergills, living half-way up Westmorland's Shap Fell, I was not long in taking this advice.

I took the train to Kendal a day later (on 23 September 1939) still feeling grim with raised temperature, but in a few glorious early autumn days on Shap recovered well enough to do some fell walking. My sister Anne joined me for the first week of this Westmorland break.[2]

Fully recovered, I resumed house officer duties in mid-October, back at Hill End Hospital where my medical firm was now based. Until the end of the year I concentrated on increasing my competence in general medicine, feeling that this was how I could best serve the war effort at that time. In the next two years I was committed to becoming a member of the Royal College of Physicians (of London) and a more useful clinician. I had no immediate thoughts of joining the Royal Army Medical Corps, believing that I lacked adequate experience.

In these early months of the War I began seeing more of Louisa "Lou" Seely, who was to become my wife. She was the youngest daughter of Jack Seely, Lord Mottistone. We had known each other for several years. Her step-brother, John Nicholson, had been one of my Cambridge friends. Our first meeting had been at a Trinity May Week Ball seven years earlier (in 1932) which she attended with John. Following that we had met on several occasions when I was John's guest at their Isle of Wight home,

Mottistone Manor, when nothing more than fondness had developed. That is how it might have remained if we had not met at two or three dinner parties soon after I qualified and decided to stay in touch, which led to several enjoyable theatre dates. Not until the fourth or fifth of these, which was a splendid London performance of the *Beggar's Opera*, did I realise how attractive this young woman was. From that point a loving relationship developed.

I learned later that Lou had been attracted to me since my first visits to Mottistone Manor, but thought that a Cambridge rowing Blue would have too many attractive admirers ever to notice her. How times change. By November 1939 she had become one of the most desirable women I knew.

Since 1937 she had been working as a secretary at the Foreign Office in the top-secret registry of the Secret Intelligence Service, MI6.[3] Before then she had spent a summer in Vienna learning German rather than taking part in the London season as a debutante. By 1939 she was the private secretary of the deputy director of the SIS (who later became director). She spoke French and German rather well and was secretive about all that she did in her job.

Briefly relieving the gloom of the phoney war period was a Christmas Show for patients at Hill End Hospital that I helped produce. Called "Bart's at Herts", it went down remarkably well.

And for the first time I felt well paid. Under Emergency Medical Service arrangements house officers were paid £400 a year (based on what a comparable Army job would pay[4]), with board and lodgings provided. Before this, remuneration had been just £20 a year with similar benefits.

While at Hill End I looked after a delightful doctor who came in with infective endocarditis. He charmed nurses and doctors alike, a very special patient who I often stayed late talking with. At that time it was thought that the best treatment was giving heparin to stop clot formation on the "vegetation" (aggregations of fibrin, platelets, inflammatory cells and bacteria) of infected lesions of the heart valves, and using sulphonamides to combat infection, although sulphonamides were not proving very effective in such cases. He was the first patient with whom I formed a friendly attachment and then had the hurt of his loss, feeling shattered when he died. So many people died in those days of conditions that are now eminently treatable. I wrote up the case history of this doctor in the *Lancet*, my first medical paper.[5]

For my second house officer appointment, from January-April 1940, I transferred to the other sector hospital: the Colney Hatch Hospital at Friern Barnet and the firm of George "Georgie" Graham.[6] I could not have enjoyed more stimulating clinical rapport than on the firm of this highly likeable physician, both on general medicine and the care of diabetic patients in which he was a leading specialist. He had conducted research on both the chemistry and management of the disease, and been the first British researcher to describe the postprandial rise in blood sugar in diabetic patients. Before the insulin era (beginning around 1924) he had been a leading adviser on the dietary management of the disease. His Ladder Diet had been a great pre-insulin advance. The Bart's dietetics department was largely his initiative.

Choosing not to stay at Bart's for my third house officer job was considered a rash decision by many of my colleagues, who felt that my prospects of returning might be damaged. Girling Ball, the Dean of Bart's, strongly warned that "I might not get back on the ladder". But at that time I could not have cared less. I was in a curious mood wanting to move on and gain experience elsewhere, partly because the next house job in prospect at Bart's offered more of the same: general medicine.

That I settled on the idea of going to Oxford resulted from an urge to get into academic medicine and the prospect of working for Leslie Witts,[7] a former Bart's tutor who had become Oxford's first Nuffield Professor of Medicine.[8] I wrote expressing my interest in working with him at Oxford and in reply he offered me the next house job on his firm at the Radcliffe Infirmary from July to December 1940, and a junior research post until that began (from May-July). We had got on well when I was his student at Bart's and there was no hesitation in accepting his offer.

After transferring to Oxford at the end of April 1940 most of my meetings with Louisa Seely were there. Usually Lou came down by train on Saturdays when we explored sandbagged Oxford (with lots of historic buildings so protected) or punted on the Cherwell. Occasionally, I took my bicycle and went up on the train and cycled to meet her for lunch in London. Our relationship had become deeply passionate. I had never been as deeply attracted to anyone. While not glamorous in a film actress way, Lou had an irresistible combination of looks, charm, humour and caring.

Leslie Witts, whose department I joined at Oxford, was a generous chief who advised that I spend my first two months in reading recent research literature rather than pitching into a research assignment. He felt that this would assist my preparations for the MRCP (Membership of the Royal College of Physicians) Examination that I intended taking a few months later. Consequently, I spent long hours in the medical section of Oxford's Bodleian Library reading latest volumes of the *British Medical Journal*, *Lancet* and other relevant journals, but at the time of Dunkirk (at the end of May 1940) felt terribly embarrassed to be pursuing career interests, not national ones.

I was glad of the relief of becoming Witts's house physician a week later. Working in a busy provincial hospital swiftly shut out thoughts of wartime worthlessness, particularly the curious satisfaction of being drafted into blood collection in preparation for the casualties of long awaited air raid attack. This was before any national blood transfusion service had evolved, although planning was underway. On Monday afternoons I used to go to bleed dozens of donors at the New

Bodleian Library (an annexe of the Bodleian, opened in 1937), which had enough reserve space to accommodate a blood transfusion unit.[9]

It was an absolute joy working on Witts' firm. He was a superb teacher on a one-to-one basis. I would do ward rounds with him and afterwards, while having coffee in sister's room, would ask questions on particularly challenging cases and diseases and he would answer with the kind of detail of a *BMJ* or *Lancet* leading article. He had amazing and easily accessed stores of knowledge. But he was not such a good teacher of groups of students. He tended to concentrate too often on finer, less relevant points, more interesting to him than needed by them. I remember a case of diabetes in the ward when he went laboriously down the relatively obscure avenue of discussing links between diabetes mellitus and the rather unimportant condition of carotenaemia (resulting sometimes from the metabolic failure of diabetics to degrade beta-carotene, a yellow pigment causing discolouration of the skin, and in other situations from a diet excessive in carrots; even combinations of both). The students were left somewhat bewildered, as they often were. But working alongside him, day-by-day, I could not have had a better one-to-one tutor in clinical medicine.

And on occasions I had wonderful instruction from the fine young physician, Alec Cooke,[10] who later became Dean of the Oxford Medical School. The Oxford undergraduate medical school had not been long established (with about 30 students) when I arrived at the Radcliffe Infirmary, a wartime expedient ending academic Oxford's reluctance to engage in professional training. Cooke was to become one of Oxford's finest clinical teachers and a considerable expert on diabetes mellitus.

Other notable colleagues of this Oxford period of my life were Cuthbert Cope,[11] the assistant physician on Witts' firm, who was developing a reputation as a clinical endocrinologist, following early research on kidney functioning, and Douglas Black,[12] a fellow Nuffield research student impressively assisting Witts with a number of haematological studies.

Witts' firm had about thirty beds in two wards at the Radcliffe Infirmary and about half way through my six months as house physician I shockingly found myself a patient in one of them. This was after a progressively thirsty Sunday and Monday and peeing rather a lot. My concern heightened steeply at the end of my blood collecting session at the New Bodleian Library on Monday afternoon when instead of having one cup of tea as usual I had four or five in swift succession. Anxious to rule out a suspicion that I had become diabetic, I went straight back to the Radcliffe Infirmary and did a Fehling's test on a sample of my urine (for excreted glucose). The shock of seeing vast amounts of brick-red precipitate billow-up as I boiled the sample with Fehling's is hard to describe. I remember saying to myself this is ridiculous, this only happens to patients, not me! I remember going off and showing Robin Hill, another Nuffield Research student (later a senior researcher in nuclear medicine at Harwell) the test result and he remaining desperately quiet, not knowing what he could usefully say at this grim moment. He just went on with his pipetting.

Witts was up in London, but I was admitted to the ward and given an injection of insulin. The swift, effective management of my diabetes restored confidence that I would be able to go ahead with the MRCP Examination due a month later, but Witts felt that I would be wiser to delay the demands of this and go on holiday instead, recommending that I wait until the next sitting of the Exam in April, 1941, which is what I did. I went up to Westmorland and had a restful fortnight at my mother's family home, Ellergreen, and then returned to Oxford and got on with my job as house physician.

I also helped to write and produce an outrageous hospital pantomime, *Dick Whittington and his Dog*, for Christmas 1940, and with two enthusiastic colleagues, Charles Scott Russell (who became professor of obstetrics at Sheffield) and James Angell (who became a consultant urologist), founded the Tingewick[13] Society (a medical students' pantomime drama group, initially known as the Pink Elephants) which has gone from strength to strength in putting on hospital pantomimes at Oxford in every year since. (Alastair Robb-Smith, one of the original group and later a distinguished Oxford pathologist, came up with the name Tingewick.)

The pantomime plot was of Dick Whittington abandoning London to find a better life at Oxford, leaving his girlfriend desolate and searching for him desperately and unsuccessfully. Trapped into vice, she is rescued by two fairy policemen who miraculously transform her into a dog called Menopause to save her from prostitution, and spirit her to Oxford and Whittington's side to steer him from the unhappiness he has found there. His happiness is complete when Menopause magically transforms back into his girlfriend. In this production I shared a scene with Charles Scott Russell in which we put on a show of tap-dancing interspersed with a comic review of various senior members of hospital staff.

In just a few weeks I had gone from the shocking discovery that I had diabetes mellitus (Type 1 diabetes) to the hilarity of performing in pantomime. Apart from the inconvenience of insulin injections, the disease was to make remarkably little difference to my enjoyment of life and career development.

I have recently been looking through a rather dilapidated score of the 1941 Tingewick pantomime that I helped script and have pulled out a few lines by the Fairy Godfather as he transforms Cinderella (a bullied nurse) for the Ball. They typify our efforts:

Come ye spirits of romance,
Come ye elfins of the dance,
Come ye little gnomes who weave
Dresses out of make-believe.
First of all – you disperse
All the trappings of a nurse,
Then out of nature's raw material

34

Fit her out in clothes ethereal.
Out of early morning air
Weave a silken brassiere,
Then let thistledown be pressed
Into the fabric of a vest.
From a starlight beam that flickers,
Weave a pair of frilly knickers.
From strands of spider's web that float
Weave for her a petty coat.
From evening light that warmly glows
Weave for her full-fashioned hose,
And from moss, the softest ever felt,
Make a strong suspender belt.
Skins of dragon flies you'll use
For her tiny little shoes.
Moon and sunbeams now impress
For a dazzling evening dress.
Lastly, may this wand of ours
Waft her the scent of flowers,
Which like nectar may entrance
All who meet her at the dance.
The transformation is begun,
Prestissimo... and it is done.

I still think this is rather good, but suspect that it was written by my far brighter co-writer, James Angell, who wrote much of this script.

1941 was a truly vintage year. By extraordinary chance, I became the first clinician in history to witness the miraculous potential of penicillin. And just a few months later had the extraordinary good fortune of marrying Louisa Seely.

How I came to conduct the pilot clinical trials on penicillin is a remarkable example of being in the right place at the right time. I have had this kind of good fortune on several occasions. Sheer coincidence drew me into the penicillin story in January 1941. I knew little of the penicillin project until, on a mid-January day, I called at Witts' office with some paperwork and was invited in to meet Howard Florey,[14] the project's leader.

The small team of scientists that Florey led at Oxford's Sir William Dunn School of Pathology had made its wartime quest the isolation of penicillin, the strongly antibiotic substance secreted by the mould *Penicillium notatum*, with hopes of it proving of massive therapeutic value. Wonderfully innovative and resourceful, his team had overcome major early difficulties in extracting penicillin (a highly unstable beta-lactam) from the culture medium of the mould into which it was secreted in miniscule quantities. Using scarce early supplies, the team had shown its amazing effectiveness in combating life-threatening streptococcal infection in mice. Since then the challenge had been in acquiring sufficient supplies of the antibiotic for clinical tests. For this the laboratory had needed to transform into a factory culturing the mould in hundreds of bedpan-like vessels, biscuit tins originally, just to accumulate a few grams of antibiotic for pilot testing on cases of severe streptococcal and staphylococcal infection.

The conversation between Witts and Florey that I interrupted was about getting these tests under way at the Radcliffe Infirmary. Witts had been asked to take this on. Knowing that I was short of a research project he quickly decided that I should. I had recently come to the end of my house job on his firm and was back as a Nuffield research student in his Department considering research options. "Here's your man", he told Florey. "Fletcher can do the testing." Becoming involved was as simple as that.

Witts can not have envisaged the historic role that he was giving me. Not even Florey could have envisaged the full magnitude of what I was to reveal.[15]

The first essential clinical test was that of proving that the penicillin being produced at the William Dunn School was safe to give to patients. Side effects were a serious and feared possibility and could even have been fatal. Who to give it to was a major ethical dilemma. It was Florey and Witts who decided that the initial test should be on a patient with limited time to live who agreed to take the risk in the interests of medical research. I chose a woman

(Elva Akers) who was dying of inoperable cancer, with only a month or so to live, and she agreed to be injected with the antibiotic. There were no ethical committees then and I needed no other permission.

Records show that on 17 January 1941 I gave her an injection of 100 milligrams of penicillin intravenously, while Witts and Florey looked on. Unfortunately, the antibiotic was not pure enough and she had a sharp rise in temperature and a rigor (a shivering attack) about an hour and a half later, showing that there were still pyrogens in the penicillin sample used. A rather unhappy Florey returned to his team at the Sir William Dunn School of Pathology to get more rigorous purification of the antibiotic under way.

With purer supplies produced, I set about testing the best way of administering penicillin. Giving it by mouth was soon ruled out. It did not survive passage through the stomach. Tests of intravenous, intramuscular and rectal routes showed intravenous injection to be the best way.

By then we were ready to treat a severe case of bacterial infection and early in February I found one of remarkable severity in the Hospital's septic ward. All major hospitals had septic wards then for victims of severe septicaemia (bacterial infection of the blood), many of them with grimly discharging abscesses. Mainly, sufferers had dangerous staphylococcal infection causing great pain. Septic wards were places of misery.

Florey had advised that I treat the worst case that I could find and this was of severe staphylococcal and streptococcal infection in a 43-year-old Oxford policeman (Albert Alexander). The infection had begun in a small scratch on his face due to contact with a rose bush and had led to numerous facial abscesses. This was a time when such scratches could have fatal consequences. He had been on the septic ward for several weeks and treated with massive doses of the best anti-bacterial drug, sulphapyridine, without any effect. When I saw him on the 12 February 1941 his eye had recently been removed due to the spread of infection, which had now reached his right shoulder and lungs. I judged that he had only days to live.

I began giving him intravenous injections of penicillin without delay, beginning with a dose of 200 milligrams, the largest that I had given, based on Florey's calculation of an appropriate first injection for a man of his stature. This was followed by 100 milligram injections three hourly. The nearest I ever came to seeing a miracle was in witnessing this patient's dramatic improvement. After 24 hours he looked considerably better and was able to sit up and eat. By the fourth day he looked on the way to full recovery. Lazarus being raised from the grave could not have been much more impressive. But regrettably our penicillin supplies ran out on the fifth day and about a week later he relapsed and never recovered. Treatment had not completely eradicated the infection by the time it prematurely ended.

Supplies of penicillin were a critical limiting factor. The penicillin laboriously extracted from about a thousand litres of mould culture medium was only enough for a day's injections. Although Florey's team at the William Dunn School supplemented the scarce supplies available by laboratory reclamation of every milligram of penicillin in the patient's urine each day, we ran out too soon. We all shared bitter disappointment at the patient's death, but elation also that penicillin had proved vastly more effective than we had dared to hope.

I have vivid memories of cycling from the Radcliffe Infirmary to the William Dunn School of Pathology each evening with bottles of the patient's urine for penicillin extraction for re-use, and Florey and his colleague Ernst Chain[16] anxiously asking how the patient was progressing. Florey, a laconic Australian, contained his delight well as penicillin revealed its colossal therapeutic potential. "That's good" he would comment, while Chain was excitedly jubilant, in his mid-European way.

Over the next four months (February-June 1941) I treated a further seven patients with penicillin. Most were children to whom I could give smaller doses of the antibiotic and so maximise the limited supplies that Florey's team laboriously produced.

The first child that I treated was a young teenage boy of 15 who was desperately ill with septicaemia resulting from an infected surgical hip wound (following pinning of the hip). Sulphonamides had not relieved his condition and I decided to test whether penicillin would. Again, the result was astounding. Within two days of starting the treatment (on 22 February 1941) he was feeling much better and remained so until the hip pin that had caused the infection was removed a month later.

Equally remarkable results followed the treatment of a man with a gigantic carbuncle on his back (from 3-10 May, 1941). We don't see carbuncles nowadays: clusters of boils usually with numerous pus-discharging heads, resulting from severe localised staphylococcal infection of the skin. This one was about four inches wide and causing great pain. Typically, recovery was expected to be slow, over at least a month of hospital care, with various dressings being applied, but I decided to test the effectiveness of penicillin and the difference was recovery in a week. Daily, one watched the carbuncle shrinking.

The most appalling case that I treated with penicillin was of a boy of four who was dying of cavernous sinus thrombosis. I still remember the grim, cat-like cries that he was wailing. Infection that had begun locally on the face had spread to the cavernous sinus, a cavity behind the eye ringed by numerous thin-walled veins, and resulted in a blood clot there. Watching this small boy recover from a virtually fatal condition was among the most memorable moments of my career. This was in the second half of May (from 13-22 May 1941).[17]

Tragically this boy died of a brain haemorrhage a week later, due to the rupturing of a weakened blood vessel. But from the post-mortem examination we had confirmation that the infection had been completely eradicated.

By then the amazing potential of penicillin was indisputable. I remember saying to Florey "Sir, it must be marvellous to have achieved a medical breakthrough like this" and his typical no-frills reply "Yes, it doesn't happen to everybody and I don't suppose I'll do anything like it again, but it is nice to have happened once in a lifetime".

Unfortunately, the magnitude of penicillin's potential was not grasped by the Medical Research Council and leading drug firms in Britain, who largely resisted Florey's requests for help in speeding penicillin research and technology towards large-scale production. He ran into enormous myopia in trying to promote its development, with key figures in research-funding and heads of pharmaceutical companies unable to perceive the importance of penicillin to the war effort, particularly its capacity to heal war wounds and get troops back into action more swiftly than ever before. Sir Edward Mellanby,[18] my father's successor as head of the Medical Research Council, has to be black-marked for his failure to recognise the importance of penicillin production. It was the great black spot on an otherwise illustrious career. The lack of British interest in penicillin production led to Florey seeking American collaborators and the antibiotic's first commercial production being in the USA, not Britain, with consequent colossal loss of revenue to this country.

In addition to the tests of penicillin that I have mentioned, I also treated a urinary tract infection in a baby[19] and several cases (4) of acute eye infection at the Oxford eye hospital, all successfully. But by June 1941 penicillin production in Florey's department developed problems. Pressures of penicillin production had exhausted the team and supplies and my involvement ended.

I was dismayed and delighted to be named on the landmark penicillin research paper published by Florey and his team in the *Lancet*[20] a short while afterwards. My part had been so minor that I questioned my inclusion, but Florey insisted on the publication being by the whole team: Abraham, Chain, Fletcher, Gardner, Heatley,

Jennings, Florey. And later, through Florey's generosity, my name was included in the list of penicillin pioneers in the memorial garden established at Magdalen College, Oxford.[21]

Only later did I learn of tensions between the discoverer of penicillin, Alexander Fleming, and the Oxford team. They resulted from Florey's team taking on research that Fleming had never got around to. His penicillin research had long lapsed (back in the early 1930s) when the Oxford team set out to find just how therapeutic this antibiotic might be. This involved the monumental challenge of isolating pure penicillin and laboriously garnering quantities enough for clinical tests. Fleming's aspirations had never stretched that far. The Oxford team believed that he was gone from the research field when it took up the story. But as soon as it began publishing its amazing findings, Fleming popped-up, reminding everyone of his pre-eminence in it.

He was remarkably ungenerous to Florey; regarding himself as the discoverer and Florey as just the technician who had got hold of his idea and developed it. I interviewed Fleming for a BBC television programme (Panorama on 12 January 1955 [22]) two months before he died and he would not say a word about the Oxford side of the story. But history will recognise the greater debt due to Florey's team, which translated Fleming's epic discovery of 1928 (that the mould *Penicillium notatum* exuded a strongly antibiotic substance) into the greatest therapeutic advance the world had known. Fleming could not have done this. It needed a team approach. That would not have been his way.

My part in the penicillin story was a very minor one, but an awesome experience. Few clinicians in history have been as privileged. My involvement with the Oxford team gave, at last, a sense of contributing to a worthwhile wartime initiative and combated an uneasy view of myself as a man building a career while others fought. With my diabetes ending the possibility of serving with the Royal Army Medical Corps, I needed clinical ways of being relevant. Over the last winter, with bombs raining down on London and most industrial cities, my clinical life in Oxford had too often felt like being parked in an easy-street of self-interested career development. There was a surreal feel to being in a quiet and ancient university town while so many other towns and cities were being flattened, although Oxford had a sizeable influx of refugees from the industrial south coast towns and queues for scarce supplies of food every day.

I became a member of the Royal College of Physicians in the period in which I was testing penicillin. I went up to London for the week of the MRCP examinations in April (1941) and saw something of the devastation of the bombing. Lacking a good long-term memory, I had packed as much revision as possible into the month before. My memory stacks well, like a mild steel blade taking a sharp edge, but soon loses its sharpness for detail. I have never been able to remember favourite poems for long or the lines of parts that I have played on stage. Favourite sonnets I have to keep relearning.

The written papers of day one of the MRCP examination went well, even a compulsory translation; German to English in my case. There were one or two puzzling specimens to discuss in the first *viva voce* examination two days later: a kidney on which I did not spot small white spots and a chest x-ray showing opacities the like of which I had not seen before. Fortunately, the *viva voce* skills that I had cultivated saved the day. I had found that examiners tended to break the silence first if one went on examining a specimen intently without comment for several minutes. This I did in the case of the puzzling kidney until the examiner cracked and asked what I thought of the small white spots, which was the clue I needed to identify periarteritis nodosa. In the case of the x-ray, I resorted to polite frankness, saying that I had not seen anything like it, to which the examiner replied: "Thank God for frankness. Most candidates have wrongly gone down the route of thinking it must be TB". Well-timed frankness can be an important weapon in *viva voce* exams, once reasonable rapport has been established with the examiner. In the end, I came out of the examination with high marks, details of which I had from my uncle, Herbert Morley Fletcher, a senior member of the College.

Leslie Witts deserved much of the credit for this success. He was the kindliest clinical chief, glad always to share his knowledge and experience. I owe him a considerable debt, not just for delegating penicillin testing to me, but for the day-to-day, in-depth discussion of cases on his wards and for introducing me to gastroscopy,[23] in which I became especially interested. Also, he drew me into his social circle at a time when I had few friends in Oxford. I loved the dance parties that he and some of his friends organised almost fortnightly. They rotated around about six homes, were evening dress occasions and great fun, attended by some remarkable Oxford dons. Solly Zuckerman[24] was among them. He was in the Oxford zoology department then (1934-45), but rapidly becoming drawn into the wartime operations research that led to him becoming a Government adviser on a range of critical strategies, including bombing policy.

Inevitably, such parties left a sense of guilt that I was not sharing the nightly horrors of bombing with Lou in London. I began going up to London to see her more frequently. Occasionally, I watched the distant glow of London's nightly bombing from the top of the Radcliffe Camera, hoping that she was safe. She was living in her father's Westminster apartment at Marsham Court.

By the time that my work with penicillin ended (early in July 1941) we were both on the edge of a decision to get married. I am not sure why we dickered in deciding. We were both lovingly committed to each other, but I was slightly diffident about the final step. I talked with my sister Anne's husband, Stephan Hopkinson,[25] a remarkable man, the vicar of heavily bombed Battersea at that time, whose views I valued, and he helpfully concentrated on how compatible we would be. We were also pushed in the right direction by Lou's delightful stepmother, Evie,[26] during an early summer visit to Mottistone Manor.[27] By now the Mottistones were wonderfully supportive, although initially Lou's father had been worried about her marrying a diabetic. It was fortunate that when he sought the advice of leading physician and friend, Sir Thomas Horder[28] (physician to George VI), Horder had pronounced in my favour.

Louisa Mary Sylvia Seely, c1940

I regret that niggling uncertainties about marriage went on plaguing me for far too long and were only finally resolved when it became too embarrassing to delay a decision any longer. At that point (the beginning of August 1941) I took Lou to Ellergreen, my mother's family home, then the home of my uncle James "Jem" Cropper,[29] for a final decision-making weekend. I felt that Ellergreen was the right place for this. My parents had become engaged there and several of my aunts and uncles also. I felt that this house must have the right ambience for our decision. But the weekend break took off badly. There was torrential rain and I had painful problems with a wisdom tooth that kept me rather subdued for a day and a half. It was only on the Sunday that Lou and I got down to addressing our fateful decision, using a scorecard-kind of approach in listing the plusses and minuses for and against marrying, and it soon became clear that we should. At last we were engaged and on the Monday morning I went into Kendal to look for a ring. Lou had been due to travel back earlier than me, but when she caught the branch line train from Burneside on the first leg of her rail journey to London I joined her and together we chose the ring in a small antiques shop in Kendal. It had a small diamond surrounded by a ring of rubies and cost five pounds.

Looking back, I doubt whether I was in love then. I think that real love of Lou came after we were married. It was then that I knew I had made the best decision of a lifetime. Lou maintains that I considered her an ideal, caring partner for the difficult times there might be for me as a diabetic, and that this self-interest was an important determining factor.

We were married in some splendour at Winchester Cathedral on 24 October 1941 with the dean and two bishops officiating (the bishops of Winchester and Southampton).[30] Lou had been determined not to be married in bomb-scarred London where her parents had wanted the wedding to be. Her father was the Lord Lieutenant of Hampshire with a residence in Winchester,

Wedding Day, Winchester Cathedral, 1941

at the Judge's Lodgings, which seemed a far better choice. We had a very simple reception fitting the austerity of wartime rationing, with the cake decorated with rice paper due to shortages of icing sugar. The surprise for some of my Oxford colleagues attending the wedding was the rather frugal cider-cup served rather than the champagne that they had been expecting at the wedding of the daughter of a peer. My Radcliffe Infirmary colleagues Douglas Black and Molly Newhouse, later a distinguished researcher of occupational diseases, and Gwyn MacFarlane, a brilliant young haematologist, had been looking forward to rather swish catering, but their faces fell at the modesty of the spread, which was a wise public relations move by Lou's father. (The announcement in the papers said that there would not to be a reception.)

We went on honeymoon at Minster Lovell on the edge of the Cotswolds close to Oxford where we spent a week at the 17th century Old Swan Inn. I had heard that the proprietor was a diabetic and likely to provide suitable meals. We drove there in Lou's father's car. Petrol rationing and the limited number of petrol coupons that we were able to borrow from friends kept us from going further than Oxfordshire.

Through marriage to Lou I joined quite an exceptional family. My father-in-law, Jack Seely,[31] was a splendid extrovert and renowned war hero with many tales of adventure to tell, all of which he enjoyed embellishing, although none needed it; they were all amazing enough. During his career as a Liberal politician he had been a Secretary of State (for War) in Asquith's pre-World War I government and in that war had led the Canadian Cavalry regiments (with the rank of Major General) with valour that earned him *Croix de Guerre* and *Légion d'Honneur* medals. For outstanding bravery in the earlier South African War he had the DSO. Best of all, I loved hearing of his exploits as a member of the Isle of Wight lifeboat crew at Brooke (on the SW corner of the Island) where he was brought up, particularly his account of one occasion in October 1892, when he swam through mountainous waves, against which the lifeboat had been powerless, to get a rescue line to a battered French sailing vessel on nearby rocks: a feat that saved lives and earned him France's highest civilian bravery award, (*La Médaille d'Or d'Honneur*) as well as cracked ribs and a torn lung, of which he made light.[32]

You have only to read his great book *Fear and be Slain* (1931)[33] to see what sort of man Jack Seely was. In it are references to his gallant horse *Warrior*[34] on which he rode in World War 1. But the last chapter of Jack Seely's life, when I knew him, was blighted by the extent to which he had backed appeasement as the best solution to the Nazi threat and been so wrong. The horrendous loss of life of World War 1 seemed to have inclined him to pacifism. As a military leader he had seen too many men killed. Lou had frequently challenged his view of appeasement, but without success.

Lou was his youngest daughter, the youngest of seven children, whose birth in 1913 had been tragically at the expense of her mother's life. From earliest days this tragic loss had bound them especially close. Jack Seely still regarded the loss of first wife "Nim" (Emily) whom he married in 1895, as his darkest experience. Fortunately, Jack's second wife Evie, the widow of his great friend George Nicholson, whom he married in 1917, was a capable and caring second mother. She was the planner of our wonderful wedding, assisted by my mother.

I had seen rather little of my mother since my final year as a medical student. She had been campaigning for Moral Rearmament (MRA) in the USA while war clouds were gathering in 1939 and five or six months after returning had gone to live in Cheshire, at Tirley Garth, a large country house about 2 miles from Tarporley, which had recently become the Moral Rearmament Movement's headquarters. (This fine house had been put at the disposal of the MRA Movement as a safe haven for its headquarters in wartime by Irene Prestwich, the daughter of a director of Burberry's and a devoted member of the Movement.) As a leading light in MRA my mother had quite a nice apartment at Tirley Garth and enjoyment of its fine gardens. I had visited her several times but mainly kept in close contact by sending her detailed notes on what I had been doing, keeping her in the picture, week by week. I had found an excellent way of doing this. Instead of keeping a diary, I used to make notes on my daily activities and thoughts about various people and events in a small, lined duplicating book that had a carbon paper insert that produced the copies I sent to her ("Challenge" Duplicate Book with 100 leaves in duplicate, 21cm x 14cm x 1.5cm). This was always in a pocket of my white coat at the hospital ready for the latest entry. I went on keeping daily records in this way until the 1960s, keeping mother in touch with all that I did, preserving a rich closeness. I still have these notebooks, more than 40 of them, to look back on earlier years. I recently re-read the notes on my first months as a house physician in the volume covering July-November, 1939. The notes of 4th August, 1939, are included as a postscript to this Chapter.

On returning from honeymoon we lodged in Walton Street, Oxford, with my landlady, Mrs Callow, who managed to provide a much larger room, and Lou went to work at Mansfield College where the Foreign Office had located its under-cover, wartime mapping unit to which she had managed to transfer. There, in 1942, maps for the invasion of Italy began to be drawn up. But the most unforgettable moment of her Foreign Office years had been in London when Paris fell (in June 1940) and she saw the final teleprinted message come through from France saying: "We are off now. Good bye".

I continued working as a senior Nuffield research student (an Oxford University employee) at the Radcliffe Infirmary until early in 1942, principally advancing my gastroscopy skills. Use of the gastroscope was fairly new and primitive then. For about a year I did all the gastroscopy for Witts' firm. But by 1942, I was restlessly ready for greater clinical responsibility and arranged to return to Bart's and the Friern Barnet sector hospital (within the Bart's sector of the wartime Emergency

Medical Service) where my former chief, George Graham, was the medical superintendent. I was appointed to a registrar's post at Friern (beginning in March 1942),[35] but with more than half of the consultant staff lost to War service my job at the age of 31 was effectively that of a consultant, only three years after qualifying. Just two months into this appointment I took on the responsibilities of consultant physician at the 120-bed Woolwich Memorial Hospital,[36] London SE18, which was served by Bart's physicians. I took over the beds of two consultants away on war service with the RAMC: Ronald Bodley Scott[37] and Edward Cullinan.[38] I was the only consultant physician visiting that hospital for the rest of the War. I visited once each week, always on Fridays, and had the support of a splendid young Irish woman as registrar and a resident Nigerian house officer. Nowadays this would be considered woefully inadequate medical staffing for the care of 50-60 inpatients, but in those days there was far less that medicine could do and particularly difficult cases I could refer to Bart's.

Officially at Friern, where I was based, I became George Graham's assistant physician, but with many of the hospital's senior physicians drawn into the RAMC often served in a consultant capacity, although always with Georgie Graham a kindly senior aid. We became very good friends in the war years at Friern. We were both Trinity College men and enjoyed playing golf together on occasional days off. His expertise on diabetes mellitus made him a valued adviser on my own care. He helpfully discussed with me a hyperglycaemia puzzle troubling me in early months at Friern when I had raised levels of sugar in my urine always on Fridays, despite constant careful regulation of my diet. This we attributed to the much higher responsibilities I had on days at the Woolwich Memorial Hospital, when the stresses clearly countered the effectiveness of the insulin taken. It was at that point that I became less fussy about diet. Until then, I had fastidiously weighed all the components of every meal on a weighing scale kept on the table. Instead, I became more thoughtful about stresses and varying insulin needs as well as diet.

I also learned from Georgie Graham an excellent way of easing the distress of new diabetic patients about to begin insulin injections. He began by asking them to do a first injection (of sterile saline) into the arm of a house physician who had been instructed not to flinch, which was a useful and helpful first experience of injecting. Then he told them of blackberry pickers being frequently pricked but getting used to it and not noticing.

Georgie Graham was a bachelor aged about 60 then, whose good-natured and trusting disposition made him an ideal target for practical jokes, all of which he took with remarkably good humour. I remember Brian Brook, who became the professor of surgery at St. George's Medical School London gleefully advising him, after he had suffered a succession of heavy colds, to read a recent *BMJ* article that might be helpful. This was an article on the psychology of colds that hypothesised that recurrent colds were commonest in the sexually deprived. Hardly a day went by without Brook asking whether he had heeded its revelations. A prank I played on him was planting a sunflower in a window box at his hospital apartment while he was away on a short break, leaving him delightfully bemused as to its origins. Initially, to everyone's amusement, he thought that it might have shot up from a seed deposited by a bird as some of the weeds had. He spent a puzzled week until I confessed that it was from my garden.

1942 was the year in which my interests in gardening began. Until then I knew nothing about it, but soon after returning to Friern Lou found us a small semi-detached house to rent and this had a longish narrow garden where I began growing vegetables to boost our rather meagre wartime rations. Helped by Martin Wright, my best man, I also built a hen house for Lou to keep a dozen hens, which were all given the names of hospital colleagues. In my gardening I was fortunate in having a very good gardener living next door and his regular over-the-fence instruction.

Among the happiest years of married life were the ones spent at 34 Church Crescent in Muswell Hill. Despite the grim décor greeting us when we moved into it early in January, 1942, we felt lucky to have snapped up one of the few small houses being rented locally. We had few items of furniture, the electric fire in the living room was the ugliest I have ever seen, and there were gloomy blackout shutters made of plasterboard to be tacked to the window frames each evening, but it was our first home and the beginning of playing house together. Neither of us had the slightest experience of running a home, so it was all exploration and adventure doing things we had never done before. Lou's cooking had some hilarious early flops, but steadily improved. My DIY skills soon advanced to brightening the rooms with whatever wartime paint we could acquire. Then from the furniture that my mother had put in store when she moved out of her London home, she suggested we select what we needed to complete the furnishing. Lou still talks of us creating a love nest there in 1942, the year in which our first child, Mark, was born on 3rd October at a local nursing home, although not on time and not without difficulties. He should have arrived a fortnight earlier and his birth was difficult because Lou had an awkwardly shaped pelvis that complicated labour.[39] From about the time that his birth was due, I used to arrive home in the evening to Lou's increasingly despairing greeting: "No baby, no eggs". The hens were obstinately not laying.

Becoming a father was a great moment and another step in the erosion of my self-centredness that marriage had begun. I had grown up achievement and career-centred, rarely thinking of others more than superficially, except Lou and my mother, but Lou introduced me to a whole new dimension of thoughtfulness. She picked-up on other people's problems and sensitivities as I never could, although slowly over the years I improved in this kind of perception and consideration, to the advantage of relationships with patients and colleagues.

What I discovered later was that Lou had recognised the challenges there would be in life with a career-centred diabetic and was resiliently and lovingly prepared for all of them. And during the war years at Friern she took in her stride many lonely nights when I was on overnight duty at the hospital, some when there were bombing raids. From 1942-1944, I worked a pattern of two nights on and two nights off, in addition to daytime duties.

Before Mark was born in 1942, I began going once each week to the Central Middlesex Hospital to work with Francis Avery Jones[40] who was developing an impressive gastroenterology department there and had agreed to advance my gastroscopy skills. We had similar backgrounds at Bart's and in working for Leslie Witts, who had introduced both of us to gastroscopy (Avery Jones in 1936) and so we were off to a good start when I asked for his help. I also began my morning-a-week visits to his department with the advantage of my own state-of-the-art, Herman Taylor semi-flexible gastroscope, the purchase of which my mother had funded from a windfall of £100 that she received in compensation for the loss of family silver by the firm that had been storing it. The gastroscope cost almost all of this.

I admired Avery Jones' bravery in choosing to make his mark more swiftly at a less prestigious county hospital rather than taking the slower climb to eminence at Bart's. His expertise in gastroscopy was equally impressive.

My advancing gastroscopy skills proved useful back at the Colney Hatch Sector Hospital at Friern Barnet where radiology facilities were second-class and had resulted in a lot of ulcers being missed. Even the fairly crude gastroscopy of that time made ulcer detection more reliable and in most cases I was able to report with some confidence whether ulcers were malignant or innocent. I examined about a thousand cases during wartime years at Friern and the Woolwich Hospital and kept detailed records, including little water colour sketches of the gastric ulcers that I saw. Occasionally in early days my technique let me down and there was one sad fatality at Woolwich when I split a woman's oesophagus. Fortunately, a kind coroner obscured my part in this by emphasising that the ulcer was malignant and would have been fatal, although my observations were not that definite. For me it was a sad lesson in the risks of a difficult procedure.

The only formal teaching in my career was in this wartime period when I gave revision lectures called "grinds" to Bart's students at Friern who were preparing for finals, and I have been glad of feedback down the years indicating that they were valued as much as I enjoyed giving them.

I also enjoyed speaking in favour of a national health service being formed, as recommended by the impressive Beveridge Committee Report published (on 2 December 1942) around the time that I arrived at Friern. As the influence of this report gathered momentum, I spoke at one or two debates in London (one of them at the Athenaeum Club) on the need for fairer health care, very much out of step with most of my hospital colleagues who despaired of losing private practice, although Georgie Graham was not among them. I was appalled by the commercial racketeering that blighted medicine. I remember one of my Friern colleagues, who knew that I had met Sir Arthur Hurst during my time at Oxford (where Hurst was a wartime consultant at the Radcliffe Infirmary), praising this outstanding physician, not for his renowned diagnostic skills, but for owning a nursing home so that he doubled the fees per private patient. I strongly wanted this kind of attitude and avarice redressed.

The darkest time at Friern was just a few months after Mark's birth, when in March 1943 I detected a swollen lymph gland in my neck and soon afterwards seemed to detect another in my right axilla. After consulting my chief, George Graham, who felt that my spleen was also slightly enlarged, there seemed a terrifying possibility that I had Hodgkin's disease, which was fatal then. A biopsy of the swollen neck gland was arranged, which I awaited with black anxiety until advised against going ahead by the hospital pathologist, Cuthbert Dukes,[41] who I was lucky to run into on my way to a ward-round. On hearing that the gland had been raised for only a month, he recommended that I delay biopsy for another two, as little would be learned from earlier investigations. More comfortingly this considerable expert, whose prognostic index[42] in colorectal cancer classification was in worldwide use, regarded my fears as premature. I owe him a colossal debt of gratitude for easing my anxiety. And a month later the glands were down and all fears of leaving my family fatherless gone. Also, prospects of the Allies winning the War had considerably brightened, with Allied forces increasingly on the offensive in 1943.

The terrors of German flying bombs shook us all in the summer of 1944, just as the War seemed in its final chapter. And some of the V-1 rockets fell rather close to home, shattering window panes. My worst moment was during a round of golf with George Graham when the sound and smoke plume from one of them crashing down seemed from the direction of our house in Church Crescent.

By the time of the V-1 rockets I had begun thinking of my next appointment. With the D-Day landings and Operation Overlord invasion of Normandy (June-July, 1944) it seemed that the final phase of the war was in progress and I was anxious to make the right move before consultants began returning from the forces and ending my spell of standing-in for them. Returning to registrar status at Bart's was not appealing and after two years of general medicine at Friern I had begun wanting to get back into academic medicine and research. Unsure of the right move, I asked the advice of Francis Fraser,[43] the professor of medicine at the British Postgraduate Medical School at Hammersmith Hospital (later the Royal Postgraduate Medical School) who at that time was serving as the medical director of the wartime Emergency Medical Service. I went up to London to see him. He had been a great friend of my father and a professor at Bart's and recommended that I apply for a temporary post that had arisen in his department at Hammersmith due to a senior lecturer going onto extended sickness leave through tuberculosis. And after a short meeting with the acting professor, John McMichael,[44] I was offered the post, which I took up in September, just before Hitler's final showering of V-2 rockets on London.

Lou, now half-way through a second pregnancy, was trying to find somewhere we could rent close to Hammersmith. She contacted all her friends and soon had the remarkable offer of a large house on the Green at Richmond-on-Thames. The mother-in-law of one of Lou's friends had bought the property a few months earlier, but Red Cross commitments in the Midlands had kept her from moving-in.[45] She had been looking for someone to take it on temporarily to end the risk of it being requisitioned by housing authorities, and kindly offered the house rent-free on the basis that we would undertake the slight bomb damage repairs that were needed as the result of a flying bomb dropping in the vicinity.

Our daughter Susanna Mary was born there on 26th January 1945, amid our improvements to the place. On that day, because there was a snowstorm, the GP had difficulties in getting there and so a nurse we had employed to help Lou with the new baby played a major part in assisting her through difficult and painful labour. After acquiring ether from a local chemist and an ether mask from a doctor living next door, I gave a light anaesthetic. When she came round from this she had a moment of horror imagining that she had lost the baby, which the nurse was out of the room tidying, but seconds later Susanna was in her arms; a moment that she described as among the most wonderful of her life. Scottie the nurse became a great family friend.

Mark, our two-and-a-half-year-old son, was away at the time of his sister's birth, which may have been a mistake. We had sent him with a treasured old nanny to stay with one of Lou's sisters on the Isle of Wight in the last week of Lou's pregnancy and while she recovered, and I suspect that even as a two-year-old he resented being sidelined for almost a month at an important time.

We had a costly winter at our large Richmond home due to hefty heating bills, high rates, repairs that were

56

needed and Lou's need for more help. With my salary remaining almost the same as in the Friern job (about £600pa) we struggled. The main reward of moving to Hammersmith Hospital was working with John McMichael, an exceptional medical scientist, and being inspiringly drawn into the research that he was conducting. At 40 he was seven years my senior.

With a research colleague at the Hammersmith he had recently pioneered cardiac catheterisation in Britain (the massive technical advance achieved in New York in the early 1940s by Cournand and Richards) and I joined him in clinical studies of catheterised hearts from week one, investigating how various diseases impacted on heart performance. Initially, with Peter Sharpey-Schafer[46] (the grandson of the eminent physiologist Sir Edward Sharpey-Schafer), heart catheterisation had been used to investigate the effects of haemorrhage on circulation.[47] The catheterised heart yielded data never directly available before on cardiac and circulatory performance. The catheter was passed to the right atrium of the heart by way of the cephalic vein of the right arm, the right axillary and subclavian veins, then the superior vena cava, and once in place provided better data than ever collected before on circulatory dynamics and the oxygen content of blood returning to the heart. And we did all this at the bedside on the ward. Laboratory facilities at the Hammersmith were not suitable for clinical investigations. All that existed in 1944 was an office-cum-laboratory that Francis Fraser (the first professor of medicine) had established before the war in a large hut in the hospital grounds, and even this was shared with surgery and gynaecology colleagues who had not taken steps to have laboratory facilities of their own.

I worked closely with John McMichael from the beginning because other colleagues of the impressive clinical and research team that he had taken over from Francis Fraser in 1940 were either absorbed into War service or on extended sick leave. Peter Sharpey-Schafer, his senior lecturer, had TB and so did his junior MRC fellow Sheila Sherlock,[48] who became a leading expert on liver diseases. The depleted staff of the Medical Department that I joined consisted of McMichael and me plus a registrar and two house physicians, but managed the heavy workload of looking after three large wards.

Within a month of assisting John McMichael with cardiac catheterisation studies we had a chance to investigate the effects of a pericardial effusion[49] on cardiac output, charting how output improved as the effusion diminished. Under his direction I made most of the measurements and they were written up in a paper to the *British Heart Journal* in 1945, my first publication on scientific medicine.[50] Original observations we made at that time of high cardiac output in a patient with Paget's disease, due to more rapid circulation of blood through the patient's less dense bone, were published in 1946.

McMichael also encouraged me to continue the gastroscopy studies with Francis Avery Jones at the Central Middlesex Hospital on which I planned to write an MD thesis. I could not have had better opportunities to advance my research interests and clinical competence.

McMichael and I regularly discussed cases while travelling-in together each morning. Our homes were very close (in Richmond and Twickenham) and we went in each other's cars on alternate days to eke out wartime petrol rations. I had a cheap, second hand car by then. It was during one of these journeys, about five months into my time at Hammersmith (in January 1945), that he told me of MRC plans to establish a pneumoconiosis research unit in South Wales. I hardly knew the meaning of pneumoconiosis, but he enlightened me and added that the search was on for a director of this unit. He had received a letter from MRC secretary, Sir Edward Mellanby, asking whether he could suggest a possible candidate; an enquiry that had gone out to the heads of several medical faculties. I just hoped and prayed that he had not recommended me to lead investigations into a dust disease of miners.

He had not, but a month later I received a letter from Mellanby offering me the job, for which I had been tentatively suggested by my former Oxford chief, Leslie Witts, and by Ronald Christie, the professor of medicine at Bart's. I could not have been less grateful. At that time I saw my future shaping as a specialist in gastroenterology and intended staying in academic medicine in London. And we were happy in Richmond. South Wales seemed a world apart and so was mining and its diseases. Being chosen to set up a research unit where I did not want to be and into a disease virtually unknown to me seemed the ultimate poisoned chalice.

After asking John McMichael's advice and having confirmation that he wanted me to stay at the Hammersmith, I wrote to Edward Mellanby, thanking him for the splendid opportunity that he had offered me, but regretting that it was not in a direction I planned for my career. For a young physician of 35, still at the registrar level, it was a unique opportunity, but I was not attracted to industrial disease and had no wish to move from academic medicine and London. Lou was even more horrified by thoughts of ending up in South Wales. We both loved our new location, our family walks with the pram down to the nearby Thames, and the closeness of many friends.

But I was not comfortable with my decision and began having restless nights pondering why. I just paced up and down the landing, concerned that I had made a mistake. After a fortnight or so of this, I talked to my brother-in-law Stephan Hopkinson, whose advice I had sought about my indecision over getting engaged to Lou. During a long walk along the Thames tow-path between Richmond and Kew he astutely suggested considering the job as an opportunity to serve national interests and make up for my lack of war service, which he knew troubled me. He felt that the opportunity to look into one of the country's most threatening industrial diseases was worth further consideration. Many thousands of men had been handicapped and lost their jobs, many of them remained severely breathless for the rest of their lives. Making a difference to this seemed to justify a bold change of mind.

And so, with Lou's agreement to share this venture, I wrote again to Mellanby saying that I would take on the job if it was still available. In his reply he said: "Don't worry about leaving clinical medicine for a while because after you have been there for two or three years and solved this problem you will return with invaluable knowledge of chest disease", which shows how little he understood clinical medicine or pneumoconiosis.

My former chief Georgie Graham reckoned that I was abandoning clinical medicine for good. My uncle Herbert (Morley Fletcher) said that I could only be taking the post "for filthy lucre", as I was doubling my salary (from £660-£1200pa). But John McMichael was wonderfully supportive in pointing to what I might achieve for a major industry, and kind in suggesting that in my last two months at the Hammersmith I concentrate on preparing for South Wales and writing up my Cambridge MD thesis on "The place of gastroscopy in clinical gastro-enterology".

My gastroscope studies at the Hammersmith had included unsuccessful studies of the normal stomach lining to provide good comparative data, because normal stomachs had hardly been investigated. But this proved difficult. Although some patients were prepared to undergo such investigation to assist my research, it was psychologically difficult for them and for me to gear ourselves to undertaking a complex examination without pathological justification. I sensed that my clinical encouragement to them lacked the conviction that it normally had. Consequently, I soon abandoned such examinations.

While I was writing-up my thesis I got to know Peter Sharpey-Schafer, who came back to the department on a part-time basis. His research brilliance, like McMichael's, increased my doubts as to whether I could ever be in their class and make the grade as a professor of medicine, my ultimate ambition. They were a pretty challenging couple to emulate. But Sharpey-Schafer had an unscrupulousness I did not admire. He would use patients as research material principally and regard their treatment as secondary. I lamented this lack of consideration, although many benefited from his brightness.

My MD thesis was examined in Cambridge in June 1945 and successful. There was a short written paper and *viva voce* examination, neither of which was difficult because gastroscopy was a fairly new investigative technique on which the literature was sparse and the knowledge of the examiners no better than my own.

A few days later I went down to South Wales with Philip D'Arcy Hart[51] who had undertaken the first MRC survey of pneumoconiosis from 1936 to 1939 with the Welsh chest physician Edward Aslett. Also assisting me on this fact-finding, contact-making visit was Richard Schilling,[52] a young specialist in industrial medicine at the MRC. By then I had read the literature of pneumoconiosis.

I met the miners' leaders in Cardiff, including Arthur Horner,[53] then the Secretary of the National Union of Miners, a strong communist who used to boast of being a guest of HM Government in prison during the General Strike of 1926 (although his imprisonment was later, in 1932). And I sat there and listened to him saying that "this disease is destroying the Coal Industry and it is up to you to do something to prevent it".

Although he exaggerated, the scale of what I had taken-on began to register. Coal was Britain's prime source of power then. It fuelled the major industries and the homes. That one of the leading coalfields was losing miners to pneumoconiosis at a threatening rate was a severe cause of alarm for the national economy and the future of Welsh mining communities. With close to 20,000 miners already lost to premature redundancy, I had been set the colossal challenge of fathoming ways to safer mining in a major coalfield.

I felt I was walking into a minefield.

PS. Sample of the daily detail recorded in the carbon-copy duplicating book covering the period 8 July – 8 November, 1939, copies from which were sent weekly to Lady Maisie Fletcher. Words in brackets have been added to assist clarity.

Friday, August 4ᵗʰ (1939)
Rather late at Bart's because of packing and the arrival at breakfast of all my holiday photographs. Spent morning in wards. Looked at cases for Cullinan in afternoon after I became Senior HP (house physician) *at 12.00.*

(Ward) *Round with Cullinan. He spent long time talking about a good case of anorexia nervosa. He was rather sensitive about it but taught as badly as ever.*

Then down to OD (outpatients department) *to see how they were getting on with the film.* Amusing watching shots of various aspects of* (a minor) *operation being taken.*

Then to surgery to see if anything and found it in a state of wild activity. There had been a big gas main explosion in St. Paul's churchyard and 70 casualties of all grades of severity (mostly cuts from flying glass and stones and bad cases were coming in).

Organisation excellent and there seemed to be adequate number of doctors and students around. Every room round the surgery had 2 or 3 patients in it, either lying down or sitting while being bandaged or drinking tea. Apparently no one was killed and worst cases were those of shock.

Back to theatre where I told film men of the explosion and one of them ran off with a camera to "cover it".

Then off to surgery ward (after looking at a sputum for Martin [Wright]*) to do a paracentesis abdomen: my first one, but the case/patient was an old lady who had had it done often before and all went well.*

Dinner, then out for a moment to look at the scene of the explosion. Couldn't get very close because of police cordon, but amusing to see plate glass windows blown in quarter of a mile away and all the streets covered in glass which had mostly been swept into big piles and was being carted away.

As soon as I got back I was sent for to give an anaesthetic in OD. The men who had been admitted had recovered from shock and were going to be stitched up. Two other theatres were working and so there were no spare anaesthetists. Went in trepidation as I had never done a "solo" before and hadn't thought of anaesthetics since last November.

Harold Wilson was operating and in a hurry, so it was additionally harassing. However I did the two cases successfully, if not very elegantly. It was gratifying that it all came back (the procedure) *as soon as one started and after the second case I felt I could tackle anything. After the two cases a proper anaesthetist turned up, so I went off to bed.*

Was just going off when I was sent for to help Michael Harmer** finish off the cases as Harold Wilson was going back to bed. So I went and scrubbed up and assisted him with the sewing up of a lot of smallish gashes on one of the victims.

Tea in OD and then to bed at 1.50am, having since I went on duty been physician, pathologist, anaesthetist and surgeon in turn!

* Reference to a film crew filming aspects of life at Bart's.
** Michael Harmer MRCS, assistant surgeon, later FRCS and surgeon, Royal Marsden Hospital.

Chapter 5
Six years in South Wales building an MRC Unit to unravel the scourge of coal miners' pneumoconiosis

What I learned of pneumoconiosis before going to South Wales was mainly from the reports of a first MRC study of coal miners' pneumoconiosis conducted from 1937 to 1940 by a team led by Drs Philip D'Arcy Hart and Edward Aslett.[1] Their assignment had been to report on differences between the chronic dust disease disabling coal miners and silicosis, the chronic lung disease of men working in hard rock. Until then, coal workers' pneumoconiosis had been regarded as a variant of silicosis and disability compensation tied to silicosis being diagnosed. This had left many tens of thousands of dust-disabled miners uncompensated, a growing national concern of the 1930s leading to the 1937 MRC review that sent Hart and Aslett to investigate pneumoconiosis in South Wales where it was most concentrated.

Their main achievement had been in revealing clear differences between the chest x-rays of pneumoconiosis sufferers and silicosis victims. From a major radiographic survey of pneumoconiosis sufferers they showed the characteristic patterns of coal dust accumulation and related this to declining lung function and disability development. From their radiographic charting of disease development came a classification of developmental stages ranging from early coal dust nodulation steadily spreading through the lungs with length of exposure to dust, then the risk of a final disabling development of massive fibrous lesions seriously impeding breathing, which became known as progressive massive fibrosis (PMF). Preventing this became a principal concern of their reporting, which recommended that men be certified as disabled and compensated at one x-ray stage before this risk was reached. On the basis of this, a new certification and compensation[2] package had been introduced in 1943. Hart and Aslett had also investigated a growing view that PMF was only triggered by an interaction of well-developed pneumoconiosis and tuberculosis, but not found supporting evidence. Nevertheless, interest in the possibility of TB playing a part remained, due to close similarities between the fibrosis of TB and PMF.

The Hart and Aslett survey also provided valuable disease prevalence data, showing that the dusts of some collieries resulted in greater incidence of pneumoconiosis. In South Wales the anthracite mines to the west of the coalfield had highest disease incidence in contrast to the "house coal" producing mines of the south east of the region, which had the lowest. Far greater investigation of dusts was needed and ways of keeping levels low at a time when mechanisation of the industry was raising them. And little had been done about rehabilitating miners for future employment outside the industry. There were many challenges.

Why I was chosen by the MRC to take the lead in resolving the major industrial disease problem of that time and the single-handed way in which I was sent to South Wales to begin this, I have never fully understood. Later, I discovered that two of the professors of medicine asked about possible candidates had tentatively suggested me. I also formed the impression that Edward Mellanby, the Secretary of the MRC, had liked the idea of his predecessor's son taking the job. His initial attempts to get John McMichael interested in it had failed. McMichael had taken part in the first MRC survey.[3]

I began my work in Cardiff in July 1945, a month after war in Europe ended. By then, Lou and I had been there twice looking for houses we might buy but without success. Very few properties other than castles or semis were coming onto the market at that time. And so we accepted temporary accommodation offered by the MRC in a house that had been acquired to provide me with initial office accommodation (at 32 The Parade, off City Road, CF24 3AB) which had been a National Savings office during the war. Unaware of the grim state in which it had been left, we drove down in our small second-hand car in mid-July 1945 to get settled-in, followed by the furniture van bringing essential furnishings (the rest having gone into store). At 32 The Parade we found a property looking trashed, with fittings ripped out and remnants of torn posters adorning the walls. Rats were already in residence and our clean-up operations were to the accompaniment of clanking trams along the City Road. We were pleased to have left our children (Mark and Susanna) with Lou's friend at Hereford where we had called on the way down.

We lived in this grim MRC property for several months and when the children joined us two weeks later their clothes required frequent washing because of all the soot in the air. But on our second day at Cardiff we heard of the house that we eventually bought. We were dinner guests of David Morgan, the medical superintendent of Llandough Hospital, and he and his wife mentioned Hickley Lodge coming onto the market. A day or so later they took us to see it.

It was at Sully Road, Penarth, almost in Dinas Powys (less than a mile from the hospital) and far from impressive: a large, gaunt property that had been the home of a coal-mine owner who had built it. During the war it had been occupied by troops and become run down, but it met Lou's size criteria and had the attraction of a vast garden and cottage for domestic staff. Lou always wanted homes far too big for us, but with a lack of options I had an uncomfortable feeling that this was where we would live.

On my first visit to Wales, David Morgan had offered me a small ward (Ward 3) at Llandough Hospital for clinical studies by my new unit; an important first step. And he was the only Welsh doctor ever offering hospitality, unlike all the rest who were superficially friendly, but resentful of my appointment and inhospitable. The MRC files that I later saw had letters expressing opposition to the appointment of an English doctor to lead what they regarded as a Welsh project. And my lack of knowledge of coal mining compounded such objections.

I was not much better equipped to bid for Hickley Lodge when it was auctioned late in 1945, but eventually it was knocked down to me for £3,050 when I chanced a final offer £50 above my intended maximum.[4] The finance for this came from my mother and a bank loan that Lou had arranged, £1,500 pounds from each. Lou had become very persuasive with bank managers. Mother's contribution was the bulk of a legacy from her Aunt Mary Cropper.

As soon as we acquired the house, Lou made all the arrangements for builders and decorators to make it habitable and it was ready for us to move in about three months later (actually in the early Spring of 1946). A mistake that we made was to allow the gardener and his wife who were living in the cottage to stay on, for Mr and Mrs Jones proved remarkably unhelpful, contrary to initial indications. Mrs Jones did not help in the house as we had hoped and her husband was not particularly cooperative. Grudgingly he supplied us with vegetables from our kitchen garden and sold the best to local greengrocers.

By the time we moved into the house, I had spent the summer formulating the first steps needed in researching pneumoconiosis and getting to know as much as possible about local mining, particularly varying degrees of prevalence of the disease across the South Wales coalfield, where there was considerable variation. I spoke to a number of local chest physicians, building a view of the disease and the disability it inflicted. I had also read and re-read the reports of the MRC's original survey.[1]

At the office at 32 The Parade I had appointed Miss Mainprice as my secretary, the first employee of the new unit. As a rampant Tory she found my leftish views difficult to tolerate and lasted only a few weeks, but in that time we put the former National Savings office into working order and established a data-filing system. The front, ground-floor sitting room became my office.

A great aid in early months was the very friendly local medical officer of the Ministry of Fuel and Power, T H (Thomas Harold) Jenkins, who arranged visits to a range of coal mines and took me down them. I was fascinated by mining and began realising how interesting industrial research could be. My reception by mine managers and miners was so encouraging that I rapidly became committed to it. I remember after one mine visit having lunch with the secretary of the local miners' union and discovering his knowledge of literature, which was far greater than mine. Many people that I met on these mine visits were very impressive. I had landed in a strange and fascinating world beyond my experience.

And everyone I met in the mining industry was looking forward to post-war change: to the nationalisation of the mines and an end to the antipathy between miners and the mine owners who had treated them so appallingly. Owners who had made vast fortunes had ploughed little back into their mines, leaving them appallingly unsafe and the men working in their dark recesses grimly underpaid. For me, the mines were a revelation. Creeping along their little roadways as though at dead of night was a stunning experience.

Another early aid was a wonderful Welshman, "Jit" J.I.T. Jones, who worked in the coal industry and was appointed to liaise with me (an arrangement made by the Ministry of Fuel and Power). He had been involved in the first MRC study of mining diseases in South Wales just before the war, particularly in studies of the coal dusts involved, and provided useful background perspective.

It was not until I had a fairly clear view of the main problems needing to be solved that I felt ready to start recruiting staff to tackle them. I remember sitting in my former National Savings office in early weeks mulling over the priorities. There were four main challenges. The first was detailed understanding of pneumoconiosis: its cause and development which had puzzling aspects. Developing a more reliable system of certifying disability was a second, while a third was discovering more of the risks of different coal dusts and ways of reducing miners' exposure to hazardous ones. And finally, the new unit needed to develop guidelines on the rehabilitation and re-employment of miners who had been certified as disabled by pneumoconiosis. Many seemed capable of working in light industry and during the war a scheme for creating light industries in South Wales had been proposed: the Grenfell Scheme, named after the Minister of Mines who formulated it, David Rhys Grenfell. There was strong political pressure on the business of getting many thousands of modestly disabled miners back into some form of work instead of having them on the dole. The new research unit had to make a contribution to this. We needed to research disability levels and what certified miners were capable of.

Pneumoconiosis was not a scourge of British mining generally, but in South Wales it was a vast source of disability and premature death. The disease was most prevalent among miners employed in the anthracite mines on the western end of the South Wales Coalfield, above Swansea. Lesser incidence was in the bituminous "steam coal" mines to the north east of the region, and the bituminous "house coal" mines of the south east had the lowest levels. Knowing more about the dust of the anthracite mines was an early priority. We needed to know far more about coal dusts.

With several major challenges ahead and not quite sure where to begin I wrote to various experts for advice, including my former Oxford chief, Leslie Witts, who had advised one or two industries on health hazards during the War. In reply, he wrote me a very nice letter saying that he had a young physician working in his department who had experience of industrial medicine and might help me to get started. He could spare her for a year. During the war she had investigated the dangers of working with TNT in the munitions industry. And so, thanks to Witts, Alice Stewart[5] became my first colleague at Cardiff in the Spring of 1946 and was tremendously enthusiastic and helpful. Initially, she advised that we develop good, collaborative links with the miners and mining communities that we needed to survey. So, with the help of "Jit" Jones and the miners' union we arranged to have meetings in all the mining valleys with men who were certified as disabled by pneumoconiosis. They were held in cinemas or school halls and invitations sent out by the miners' union. In addition to building good relations with mining communities, our objective was to get data from the men by questionnaire.

We went all over the coalfield doing this and the meetings provided a wealth of data from miners anxious to help us and warmly enthusiastic about the research we planned. A local union leader would introduce us, saying: "I'm glad to introduce Dr Fletcher who has been appointed to this new pneumoconiosis research unit and he will tell you about the work he does. And I would like to say, on your behalf, how pleased we are that something is at last being done about this terrible problem". And then I would outline what we were proposing to do and how they could help. The unusual characteristic of these audiences was that they coughed all the time due to chest problems unless I made a particularly startling point when there was sheer silence, particularly when I spoke of what we hoped the outlook for miners would be and the safety measures we were hoping to achieve. Finally, we asked them to complete a questionnaire about their experience of pneumoconiosis and to say whether they would be willing to come to Cardiff for a clinical examination, which the great majority agreed to do.

At the first meeting I discovered how difficult it is to sharpen 220 pencils fairly quickly by pencil sharpener. Very soon the metal sharpener became too hot to handle and I needed to continue intermittently by pen-knife. This was the only time that we had a late start.

To get to know more about miners and their communities Alice had the excellent idea of asking if we could stay with mining families after some of our evening visits. I would never have thought of this, but such arrangements provided valuable social insights. I warmly remember the rich hospitality accorded us. On the first occasion this was by the Evan Jones family, who could not have been more generous, with my hosts moving out of their bedroom to let me have the best room, which they did for all "important visitors". Their last one had been Harry Pollitt, the secretary of the British Communist Party. After supper I remember having splendid gardening advice from Mr Evan Jones senior, who talked amazingly of "being a curator of plants", as we sat beside a blazing fire.

It was on such visits that I learned of the stresses of a miner's life down the pit: of the way they sweated while hand-hacking and cutting coal and loading it by shovel onto wagons, often in areas with too little headroom to stand up. At that time machines were only beginning to be phased into mining. Getting to know such men was inspiring. I stayed with the Evan Jones's twice.

The small mining towns of the valleys that I visited are etched on my memory: their long rows of terraced cottages stacked on the hillsides, each sending up black palls of smoke from its chimneys. And I remember as vividly the men chatting and smoking at street corners in leisure moments, all squatting on their haunches, a position in which many were used to working, some still with black faces after their latest shift at the mine. Few pits had bathing facilities for them to clean-up after work. But the cottages to which they returned had bright open coal fires and hot water to greet them. On still days the smoke from these fires hung like a blanket over the valley, grey and lifeless, while above the greyness there was beautiful countryside on the hilltops to walk in. But the air pollution, like the smoking, played its part in a high incidence of bronchitis.

In the autumn of 1945 I appointed two clinicians to assist with the x-ray assessment and physical examination of the many hundreds of certified miners who had agreed to be examined. Dr. Idris Davies had been a GP in a place called Ynysybwl, a small town close to the Rhondda, and wanted research experience in preparation for a better job when the NHS came in. He provided valuable local experience. As his colleague I appointed Dr Morrell, who had been an Army medical officer and had relevant interests in respiratory medicine. I also advertised for a radiographer to look after the chest x-ray side of the programme and appointed John Pierce, who later in his career became the senior consultant radiologist at St. Thomas's Hospital, London. With so many examinations to conduct, we finally added a further colleague to the team, Karl Mann, a Jewish clinician of outstanding competence, who sharpened all our knowledge of respiratory medicine and later became the chief medical officer of Israel. His reading of x-rays was first rate. In the interests of consistency, I got him and Idris Davies to go back through all the x-rays amassed to check our interpretation of them. This was the small early team with which Alice Stewart and I worked at Llandough Hospital. Mann tutored us all in chest x-ray reading.

While this team got on with x-ray studies and clinical examination of certified miners, the need for physiological studies of their breathlessness became the next challenge. Detailed assessment of how far their breathing was impaired was required.

Two bright young clinical physiologists whom I met when attending the Royal Society's first post-war Conversazione in London (in November 1945)[6] seemed ideally qualified for this challenge. Both John Gilson and Alex Paton, who had been engaged in wartime research at the Farnborough Research Establishment (in the RAF Physiology Laboratory[7]) expressed considerable interest in doing the respiratory physiology, but Mellanby objected to my plan to appoint them with the sarcastic remark that I should not rush into appointing every physiologist seeking a job.

This was a surprise. I had always consulted MRC headquarters about appointments although given the impression that I would have a free hand in making the appointments needed to get research under way. I had double-checked this with Mellanby's deputy, Landsborough Thomson,[8] and been told: "We'll give you your head for a time and see what numbers seem to be necessary for a satisfactory Unit". Mellanby's attitude to these latest appointments stifled the impression of having a free hand.

Around the same time I began to receive advice on Unit development from a joint committee of MRC, Ministry of Health and Ministry of Fuel and Power Advisers, which included Austin "Tony" Bradford Hill,[9] the leading statistician and clinical trials designer, who with Richard Doll later showed the link between smoking and lung cancer. This joint committee on pneumoconiosis met about four times a year, reviewed progress and considered our plans. My research staff had already begun monthly meetings to consider lines of progress.

One of them in 1946 was a study of miners' rehabilitation and re-employment prospects. With many hundreds of certified miners prematurely unemployed there was strong political pressure for this. Also, the time had come to get dust studies under way and getting advice on this took me to Porton Down (the Government Research Establishment near Salisbury) to talk with dust researchers there. During this visit I met Watson, a physicist who had invented a thermal precipitator[10] for dust analysis and persuaded him to come to Wales and begin surveying pit dusts. Initially, he had ideas of establishing quite a team, but I managed to constrain him to beginning with just a physicist and chemist (Body and Miller) and found them accommodation at Curren's factory in Cardiff's dockland, which had begun contracting in post-war years and had vacant space in one of its buildings.

The progress of Watson's group was slowed by the unsuitability of his thermal precipitator, which produced fine results but by too lengthy a procedure. In response, he devised a simpler dust sampling instrument, an aspiration pump drawing air over a strip of filter paper, the increased opacity of which provided a measure of dust accumulated in a test period. But the results were greatly influenced by particles too large to get into the lungs, giving erroneous impressions of dust dangers.

During this period I got the clinical physiologists that I needed: Philip Hugh-Jones[11] and John Gilson.[12] Philip

Hugh-Jones was sent down by Mellanby and was to be a considerable asset. He had been looking for a job and we were pleased to have him pointed in our direction.[13] Two or three months later he was joined by John Gilson and they established a respiratory physiology laboratory in a side-room of our ward at Llandough Hospital (and later took over a second side room).[14] I never understood Mellanby's initial reservations about Gilson, but when he joined us he was first rate and possibly the best appointment that I ever made. Mellanby's doubts about his suitability were quite wrong.

Heinz Wolff[15] joined us in 1946. While wondering how to progress with dust sampling we heard of the inventive talents of this young laboratory technician in the Cambridge physiology department. He was about eighteen and in an earlier post at Oxford's Radcliffe Infirmary had devised an electronic red blood cell counter for the clinical pathologist Gwyn MacFarlane. Knowing of his interest in designing particle counters I wrote to the head of his department asking whether we could have his help for a while. The reply said that he was just a junior technician and there would be no objection to his leaving to join us, which he did a month later. As a member of Watson's team he soon created a dust sampling instrument that sucked air into a small centrifuge that spun the particles onto a surrounding film surface, according to size. This machine was not entirely satisfactory, but was used until my great friend Martin Wright joined the Unit in its second year as a pathologist to undertake studies of the effects of dust on the lungs of small mammals. He devised a much better instrument that he called "the hexlet" on account of its six dust collecting chambers. This instrument separated dust by a process called elutriation and was to become the standard dust measuring device of the coal industry.

After about a year with us, we were able to help Heinz Wolff's career lift-off by recommending him for an MRC award[16] that took him to University College London where he graduated with a first in physics and physiology and from there went on to the impressive career in bioengineering (a term he invented) and broadcasting that we all know about. He and his family were last-ditch escapees from Nazi Germany just before the war.

In autumn 1946 I went with Alice Stewart to a meeting of the Association of Physicians of Great Britain and Ireland, a blue ribbon medical club, of which Alice was being made the first woman member, and each of us gave a discussion paper on the challenges of pneumoconiosis research. This resulted in several important recommendations and observations.

Soon afterwards, the Unit began investigations of miners' rehabilitation and why so low a proportion of them found alternative employment. This was one area where research lagged. Two initiatives began helping it forwards. The first was a study of fitness that could be achieved by physical training. For this we employed a former Army physical training instructor called Ballinger, who worked with several groups of certified miners and got many of them running a quarter mile with confidence and without problems. During a routine medical follow-up with one such man, I asked how he was feeling and had the reply: "Very much better, doctor". As his symptoms had not changed, I asked in what way he felt better and his reply was "spiritually, doctor". Improvement was essentially in attitude and confidence. In so many cases, being certified as disabled and unfit to work in the mines had rocked confidence. I heard of one 42 year-old miner who had walked briskly uphill to the certification board examination centre in Swansea and after being certified had difficulty in walking back downhill. Raising confidence was an important part of any rehabilitation package.

In a second initiative we employed a young and outstanding Cardiff graduate, John Treasure,[17] who later became a top advertising executive (as vice-chairman of J Walter Thompson and Co) and dean of the City University School of Business in London, to undertake a social study of miners' attitudes to re-employment. This he carried out under the direction of Philip Hugh-Jones

76

and found that the great majority of miners felt rather like beached whales when employed in jobs outside mining. Uprooted from mining ties and comradeship they struggled with other roles. Such findings set us wondering about them being reabsorbed into the mining industry in softer, low dust hazard surface jobs where they would feel at home. At that time, being certified as disabled with pneumoconiosis meant total banishment from collieries.

A short report on the social consequences of pneumoconiosis, largely based on John Treasure's findings, was forwarded to the MRC, but not published. It was drawn up by the small social work group that we had established at the Unit.

Asking Alice Stewart to go back to Oxford was one of the most unpleasant tasks of 1947. Her view of the natural progression of pneumoconiosis was at odds with the one generally accepted at the Unit and her outspokenness was getting backs up. To preserve harmony I thanked her for all that she had done in early months and advised that she return to Oxford and write it up independently, possibly in collaboration with her close friend Dr Morrell, the only colleague sharing her views. I was glad that I did this tactfully enough to preserve our friendship, which I had greatly valued in earlier months. She had been a good ally.[18]

There were two main hypotheses on the natural history of coalminers' pneumoconiosis. The simplest, that Alice supported, was of a single disease advancing from simple, scatterings of small dust nodules in the lungs in early stages, through increasing nodulation, to the eventual formation of dust-packed, larger fibrous deposits, if men continued being subjected to dust inhalation in "hard coal" and "steam coal" mines. The latter fibrous and seriously disabling stage was progressive, hence the term progressive massive fibrosis (PMF). The alternative hypothesis was of two different diseases: pneumoconiosis and PMF and the view that tuberculosis was the transformer of one into the other. A growing body of expert opinion implicated tuberculosis in the development of PMF. Chest x-rays of TB and PMF patients had significant similarities that supported this view. Jethro Gough,[19] the professor of pathology at Cardiff who had been investigating pneumoconiosis since before the war, was strongly convinced that PMF was due to an interaction of simple pneumoconiosis and TB at a sub-clinical level of infection. And the amount of TB then around in communities made the concept feasible. Except for Alice and Dr Morrell, all my colleagues at the Pneumoconiosis Research Unit shared this view, although when PMF biopsy samples were cultured the majority was tubercle (TB mycobacterium) free.

In 1946-47, this seemed the most logical interpretation of what we were seeing. Knowledge of immunology was then too primitive for us to have better insight. What macrophages did was largely unknown and so our strong views were formed in utter ignorance. Hindsight shows that Alice Stewart's were sounder.

Like Cardiff's distinguished pathologist Jethro Gough, who had studied thousands of PMF-damaged lungs post mortem, we were deceived by fibrosis resembling that of pulmonary tuberculosis.

Gough was not an easy man to get along with. In various ways he was obstructive. Even with cautious liaison it took quite a time to establish helpful links with this inferiority complex burdened Welshman. He had clashed with the MRC over earlier research and saw the new Unit as intruding on his research domain. I was pleased when international recognition began to mellow him. That was in 1950, for a remarkable technique that he and his chief technician had devised for sectioning whole lungs: the Gough-Wentworth technique on which he published in 1949. He received considerable praise for this technique, although it was rumoured that Wentworth had been the main innovator. It involved the formalin-fixing of a lung and its impregnation with a gelatine solution, which when set and cooled to near freezing, provided support for longitudinal sectioning of the entire organ by large microtome blade. Serial examination of such sections greatly advanced post mortem views of lung pathology. (The slices were mounted on glass plates for viewing.) I admired Gough and his dedicated output of publications. We were both caught-up in the challenge of understanding this modern Black Death. (Over 15,000 Welsh miners were certified as disabled by it. In some Welsh mining valleys more than 25 per cent of the workforce was certified as disabled.)

My contributions to the literature on pneumoconiosis were modest, but I did conjure-up the term that is still used to describe the coughing-up of black sputum when there is occasional breakdown of one of the large fibrous masses of PMF. I called this "melanoptysis", based on using the prefix melan, from the Greek for black (*melas*), and *ptysma*, the Greek for sputum. If I had known the Greek word for coal (*anthrakas*) then I would have coined a better word, anthrakaloptysis, but melanoptysis established itself in the literature. And the Unit gave progressive massive fibrosis its name. Before 1946 it had been variously described.

My major contribution to pneumoconiosis research was in discovering that there were colossal variations in the interpretation of chest x-rays and in working out a way of standardising the interpretation. In my first year of going through many hundreds of radiographs to appreciate the progression of the disease, I found disconcerting levels of inconsistency in how they had been interpreted (observer error). This left me concerned that some miners had been prematurely certified as disabled, while some with more pronounced shadows had been under-categorised and left working in the pits.

I had three sources of radiographs: the ones accumulated during the initial MRC survey of 1937-40, those taken by the certification boards (since disability certification came in, in 1943) and the chest x-rays of disabled miners taken by my Unit, following my visits to mining valleys asking them to volunteer for further medical examination. These recent radiographs revealed how the disease had progressed in various circumstances, some in men who had remained in dusty pits from 1937 until wartime certification as disabled. There was a whole spectrum of instructive x-rays, but too many needing reclassification through errors in earlier interpretation: observer error.

Early in 1947 I tested the level of observer error by circulating a boxed set of 100 x-ray films for categorising by the ten doctors used by the local certification board. The x-rays sent to them represented all stages of pneumoconiosis and PMF, and had typical variations in film exposure for them to cope with. There were just five categories into which they needed classifying: pneumoconiosis-free, simple pneumoconiosis, reticular pneumoconiosis, early PMF, and advanced PMF. Miners judged to have developed reticular pneumoconiosis were the men certified as disabled.

My worst fears were justified when results came in. There were too many examples of plates that should have been classified as certifiable pneumoconiosis being under-classified as simple pneumoconiosis or even as pneumoconiosis free, while some that should have been graded in the first two categories were rated as certifiable. For about 30 per cent of the sample x-rays, variations in categorisation had been as wide as two categories apart. I was so appalled by such inconsistency that I discussed it with Peter Kerley,[20] the country's top radiologist, on my next visit to London. He attributed the problems to inadequate clinicians being involved, none of whom were radiologists. In reply, I asked whether he and one or two senior colleagues would undertake the same exercise, with the same set of films. This was arranged, but contrary to his view that inconsistencies would be largely reduced, they were not. Top radiologists were capable of similar levels of inconsistency. He was shocked by the results.

What we did in response to the problem was create an atlas of radiographs clearly typifying each category of dust disease in miners, based on the average view of a very large number of pathologists and chest physicians. This exercise was brilliantly arranged and managed by a young statistician from Oxford, Peter Oldham, who Professor Bradford Hill, a member of our advisory committee, recommended. Then, in finalising the nomenclature of the system of classification we promoted, I had the good fortune to meet Cuthbert Cope (with whom I had worked at Oxford) on one of my visits to London. After war service as an RAMC Lt Colonel he was working at the Hammersmith Postgraduate Medical School and said "Why don't you just give each category of radiograph a number?" And this we did, instead of continuing searching for descriptive terminology. There were three categories of simple pneumoconiosis in our new system of classification: 1-3, and certification became firmly fixed on removing men from the mines before they reached category 3. It was clear that only miners reaching category 3 could advance to the worse fate of highly disabling PMF, which had grimly increasing breathlessness leading finally to heart failure. Some PMF sufferers that I met were still in their early 40s. The main objective of my Unit was preventing this horrendous lung disease and improving its radiographic detection. Reducing the numbers of false positives and unnecessary redundancies was a high priority.

With the coal industry recently nationalised (a National Coal Board having taken over the management of all coal mines from 1 January, 1947) the prospects of all miners being kept under routine, annual chest x-ray surveillance had improved. And the Coal Board was not long in adopting our new radiographic classification of pneumoconiosis and PMF, after it was published in 1948.[21] As soon as it was used by the Pneumoconiosis Certification Board, certification became far more reliable. Miners whose chest x-rays had reached Category 2 of the classification were certified as disabled and compensated to save them from progressing to the next category, Category 3, with which the risks of PMF seemed associated. And on the basis of what we had discovered about disability in certified miners and the potential of many to go on working in the industry they loved, the embargo on them continuing in Coal Board employment was lifted (by an amendment of the National Insurance Act). They were slotted into jobs of low dust hazard, saving many from joblessness.

And the National Coal Board (NCB) was resolutely committed to reducing dust levels in the mines. This was mainly by water spray methods of damping it down, and had been since 1930s research had emphasised the dangers of heavy dust exposure. The need for damping-down the dust had become even greater with the ever increasing dustiness of mechanised coal-cutting. When I first arrived in Wales, different coal companies had different levels of commitment to dust-damping, but nationalising the industry brought more rigorous and cohesive dust reduction policies to the mines. At that time, the dust studies being made in my Unit were still at the stage of identifying differences in the dust composition of various mine workings. But we were no nearer to fathoming what made some dusts especially dangerous.

1948 was an important year for the Pneumoconiosis Research Unit, a memorable one for me and a monumental one for health care in Britain, with the arrival of the National Health Service (NHS). I had always voted Labour in support of social reform. I wanted a fairer Britain and the NHS seemed a critical step towards achieving this, but the post-war opposition of the medical profession to state-managed healthcare had been phenomenal, until defused by government concessions.

I remember a meeting at the British Medical Association, just months before the new health service was due to be launched, at which Charles Hill, assistant secretary of the BMA, vehemently expressed the concerns of about 80 per cent of the profession. There was colossal paranoia among doctors about what they might lose within state managed medicine and many threatened to boycott the NHS. Bringing most of them on board the new health service was a great triumph for health minister Aneurin Bevan, who visited Llandough Hospital in the thick of the discontent.

He was opening a hospital in the Rhondda Valley (one of the first opened after the War) and David Morgan, the medical superintendent of Llandough, invited him to come and address the concerns of local doctors. It was a fascinating meeting in a room too small, where we all stood, packed together, listening to his glistening oratory in answering questions and defusing concerns. But then all the goodwill achieved he undid by a totally unnecessary parting shot warning of how unwise it would be for doctors anywhere to think of opposing the Government's plans. Having won them over this was wholly unreasonable, but I think that he rather liked getting backs up. He had recently done so at London's White's Club, a Tory stronghold, where he had concluded a convivial visit by referring to the upper social classes as vermin.

We had our own ministerial visit at the Pneumoconiosis Research Unit early in 1948 when Hugh Gaitskell, the recently appointed Minister of Fuel and Power, spent a day looking at our activities and plans, which included a new MRC building to house the entire Unit on the Llandough site. He was impressive in grasping all that we were trying to achieve and in the afternoon watched the lung capacities of certified miners being assessed in our Llandough Hospital ward. Then, before leaving, I asked whether he would like to speak to a few men sitting in a small solarium at the end of the ward while waiting to be assessed and the result was astonishing. When introduced he switched from relaxed to stiffly formal mood and spoke to six miners as though addressing a major rally, emphasising all that the Government was doing to rid mining of pneumoconiosis.

At the end of the visit he amazed me again by asking "Are there very dusty pits elsewhere in Britain where there is no disease?" We were stunned that we had not thought of this and soon afterwards began planning comparative studies of dusty mines across the country.

With a new building coming on stream for the Unit (a long, single-tier wing, extending from the hospital's Ward 3) and the planning of these comparative studies under way, I enjoyed an unexpected opportunity to visit France again; my first visit to the Continent after the War. This followed a newspaper report claiming that the French had discovered a cure for pneumoconiosis and were successfully treating miners at former sanitoriums on the Mediterranean coast. Mellanby was not long in agreeing that I should go to check on what they were doing with my wife to assist me as interpreter. Her French was far more fluent than mine.

It was delightful being abroad again after the war. We went by train, using a sleeping car that was unexpectedly luxurious. The MRC had agreed to cover expenses. We went initially to Vancé, South East of Le Mans, to talk with industrial health officials who had claimed the break-through. But nothing was further from the truth. They just had some leading physiotherapist chap who had shown ways of improving the fitness of disabled miners at two or three coastal rehabilitation centres. There was no cure for pneumoconiosis, but for Lou and me the visit had a refreshing sense of exploration, funded by the MRC; our first European excursion together, at times in holiday mood.

Holiday breaks were usually spent with our children, either on the Isle of Wight with Lou's relations at Mottistone or my relations in the Lake District at Ellergreen. Summers were mainly spent at Mottistone where the children were happiest and the weather better. We used to take the car and cross the Severn on the Beachley-Aust Ferry, the "Severn Princess", which cost just a shilling or two and was quite an adventure. Usually, I returned early. I liked being at the helm of the Unit. The immense regard that I had for miners drew me strongly and emotionally into the challenge of solving their greatest health problem. By 1948 the Pneumoconiosis Research Unit had an impressive staff of more than thirty.

With hopes of moving on in the early 1950s I wanted to achieve major inroads into the prevention of pneumoconiosis and PMF. I had promised Lou to spend no longer than five years in Wales and looked forward to continuing my career in academic medicine back in London. My original hopes of specialising in gastro-intestinal medicine had not been entirely eroded and when an opportunity arose in 1948 to write an article on the nature and treatment of indigestion for *The Practitioner*, I grasped it, mainly because it remained such a poorly understood complaint.[22] I provided guidelines that were to become widely disseminated when later published as a sixpenny pamphlet. Ten thousand were sold over the next two or three years, followed by nine or ten further reprints. (After the sale of the first ten thousand copies I was offered a crate of champagne by *The Practitioner* to celebrate its success, but took the option of a cash payment, which we used for a holiday.) It was one of my early successes in public education work.

Archie Cochrane[23] joined us in 1948. The Unit needed someone to plan and lead surveys of an epidemiological kind and provide details of pneumoconiosis incidence in mining communities, as well as data on rates of progression of PMF. In 1947 I had asked Richard Doll[24] to take on the job of epidemiologist, a term not so commonly used then, but he had just begun working with Bradford Hill in London on links between smoking and lung cancer,[25] and turned it down. This left me writing to a range of medical research centres asking who might fit the bill, and Archie Cochrane was highly recommended by the distinguished epidemiologist Jerry Morris[26] of the London School of Hygiene and Tropical Medicine.

On my next visit to London I gave Archie lunch at a small Greek restaurant off the Tottenham Court Road and invited him to take a look at the Unit. Having similar Cambridge backgrounds got us off to a good start. He had been an impressive POW medical officer in some of Germany's largest POW camps of the War and received a military MBE in recognition. Since the War he had been developing interests in tuberculosis, but the right jobs and research options had not arisen. Pneumoconiosis research attracted him because TB seemed to be implicated in its transition to progressive massive fibrosis. He came down about a fortnight later and was impressed enough by what we were doing and the fellow Cambridge physiologists he met to take the job. He had visited the Unit in its early days and been shown around by Alice Stewart and not been impressed then.

Archie eventually produced the brightest research proposal of my time at the Unit, but while settling in became a valued member of the chest x-ray reading team and developed dust-sampling interests, which prepared him for directing comparative surveys of pneumoconiosis incidence at a range of dusty collieries in 1949 and 1950 (to answer Hugh Gaitskell's parting question). He was a bit abrasive while settling-in, but admired for his passionate commitment and his war record, including service with a field ambulance unit supporting Republican forces in the Spanish Civil War. He surprised us all by lodging at a hotel in the red light area of Cardiff's dockland, attracted by its genuine French cuisine and hospitality. Quite early on, he began referring to me as "the great white chief of the Unit".

Other main memories of 1948 include the visit of a group of industrial medical officers from Germany, Lou becoming pregnant in the Autumn, and the pleasure that I had from taking over the garden after the death of Jones, the unhelpful gardener we had kept on. I could now run the garden exactly as I wished and introduce a few sheep into a small paddock area.

The industrial medical officers from Germany were fascinating people to host at the Unit. They came with a very different way of classifying pneumoconiosis, based on the reticular shadowing of chest x-rays, rather than interpreting nodulation. That this was inappropriate we demonstrated by asking them to read a batch of about fifty radiographs into which we had mixed x-rays of steel workers' lung complaints. Finding that they wrongly classified quite a number of the steelworkers' radiographs as showing stages 1 and 2 of coalminers' pneumoconiosis was a great embarrassment to them. That was the beginning of our impact on German classification of the disease (which it was pointed out had been established by a leading German specialist and professor whose views would be difficult to contradict).

Our German visitors were shocked not only by the flaws in their x-ray classification, but also by what they had seen of London, which they had believed largely destroyed by wartime bombing. How much had survived astounded them.

I used to go up to London almost every month for meetings or conferences. Usually, I stayed with my Eton and Cambridge friend David McKenna (a wartime Lieutenant Colonel who was at the beginning of a distinguished career in railways administration). Occasionally, I stayed with my mother who was living with family friends, and once or twice with my sister and her husband, Stephan Hopkinson, whose Battersea vicarage was not so comfortable. And there were occasional visits to the retreat weekends at Chiswick of a religious group to which I had belonged since Cambridge days: the Trinity Group, which met at a strange retreat house. With my religious belief no longer strong, I felt an impostor, but continued attending and enjoying the fellowship of these occasions, just as I went on attending church regularly. (Not until the mid-1950s when my religious faith had gone did I admit to becoming agnostic, but Humphrey Whitbread of the brewing family, a former Trinity College colleague who organised the retreats, encouraged me to go on attending to increase critical debate. And I am still attending, thirty years later.)

I carefully avoided mentioning my declining religious belief to my mother. That would have been too hurtful. I had let her down enough by not becoming an iconic evangelist. Whenever we met I went on giving the impression of a strongly committed Christian, just as my weekly letters did. When visiting her or when family holidays coincided with hers at Ellergreen, Lou and I managed a strongly loving pretence of religious devotion. This was less difficult for Lou whose faith was still fairly strong.

Lou was an exceptionally supportive wife. Although sometimes tired to the point of exhaustion through running a house far too large for us without adequate help and coping with young children and asthma attacks, she was always interested in what I had to report about the work of the Unit when I returned home each evening, usually after supper when we sat by the fire. Although lacking a scientific background, she developed a good grasp of what we were trying to achieve and warmly took interest in who did what. Through visits to the Unit and the dinner parties given at Hickley Lodge for colleagues and their wives she got to know them remarkably well and was an excellent sounding board on staff management issues. Occasionally, in difficult situations, her perception of colleagues assisted good solutions. She was wonderfully able to get on with everyone.

But getting on with professional colleagues beyond the Unit was difficult for us all. At Hickley Lodge we gave cocktail parties for local medical colleagues, but were never invited back to their homes. Lou and I were invited to dinner by the Scottish professor of physiology, also by a Canadian professor of TB medicine, but never offered hospitality by any Welsh clinicians, except David Morgan. He was the remarkable exception. Beneath the superficial pleasantness of Welsh associates was resentment that the MRC had arranged for a bunch of bright outsiders to research a predominantly Welsh problem. I remember Martin Wright (my wedding day best man), when he came to work at the Unit, saying that the situation reminded him of India where everyone appeared polite and welcoming, but always regarded you as a foreigner. This is how we felt throughout our time in South Wales. But we were welcomed into miners' homes.

My approach to setting up the Unit should have included better regard for local attitudes and involvement, but lacking advice and perception I concentrated insensitively on research challenges and importing the best qualified investigators that I could, who were mainly from England. And my background had given this an Oxbridge bias. If I had been wise, I would have taken the trouble to draw-in Welsh contributors, although there were limitations to the expertise available. Lou later thought that appointing a panel of Welsh advisers might have defused some of the resentment. But I still feel proud of the band of bright, youngish clinicians and scientists that I drew together in Cardiff and its progress against a complex industrial scourge. All, except Archie (born in 1909), were younger than me and in appointments at roughly the hospital registrar level.

Some of my happiest moments of this period were in the large garden at Hickley Lodge playing with Mark and Susanna, often at hide and seek. After gardener Jones's death in 1948 (when we regained the cottage for our own use) we all felt much freer to do what we wanted there and I managed the gardening with a little local help. I also introduced three or four sheep into a small paddock at the bottom of the garden, which the children loved visiting. Mark assisted with some of the garden chores and helped me in the greenhouse. Sometimes we talked of how living things functioned, as I had with my father. Once I took him with me on one of my visits to a coal mine to see the industry I was trying to help. He was about seven then and attending the small local school. We cycled together quite a lot at weekends, but during this period I suddenly lost the closeness that we had had. Something that I did drove a slight wedge between us and I sensed on that day that closeness would never be regained, which is how it turned out. Lou and I both sensed him growing away from us in this period and still wonder why. Possibly we were not even-handed enough in our affection. Susanna was beautiful and delightful enough to have lots of it.

Going to a small nearby church at Dinas Powys was what we usually did on Sunday mornings, but generally I left before Holy Communion and went home with the children. Before the end of 1948 we were expecting our third child. Unfortunately, Lou still lacked reliable domestic help. A series of unsatisfactory helpers had made coping with a large house difficult, especially when her asthma struck. At times she had needed a day or two in bed to recover from exhaustion.

Fortunately, soon after the birth of Caroline on 30 May 1949 Stefania, a friendly and efficient Italian woman joined us and proved a brilliant helper. How she got to us is not a pleasant story. A friend of Lou's sister in London who knew that she was looking for a job told her that we needed domestic help in Wales, of which she had not heard, and shockingly reassured her that it was not far from London and she would not be moving very far from her friends. So her long journey to Cardiff was a frightful shock, but she took to us and stayed. She arrived with very little English, but through many comical exchanges Lou improved Stefania's grasp of the language and learned Italian in return. There are lots of humorous family stories about Stefania and her husband, Paulo, who joined us about three months later and also helped, mainly with the garden. With Stefania resident at Hickley Lodge we had the happiest years of early married life. She provided constant and caring help and was a great aid when the children were ill.

At the time of Caroline's birth in May 1949 our first survey of a dusty mine outside Wales was under way at the Haig Colliery at Whitehaven[27] in Cumbria. I had heard that this was a particularly dusty pit with little chest disease and decided that it would be a good place to start. But getting the agreement of the National Coal Board (NCB) had not been easy. Initially NCB officials stressed the opposition there would be from miners and their Union (the National Union of Mineworkers – NUM). That was back in the summer of 1948. But I talked with Alf Davies, the head of the NUM in South Wales, who regarded this view as preposterous and checked that the NUM would be in support of what we proposed. This support removed the first rung of NCB objection and we began negotiating arrangements for a first pit survey. I went with John Gilson to Whitehaven to check the suitability of the Haig mine and went down and out under the sea on this preliminary visit, confirming its high dust status.

Afterwards, we talked with the medical officer of a nearby haematite mine,[28] about the use of an x-ray unit that he had developed for routine surveillance of its miners, who were at risk of silicosis. Lacking a mobile x-ray unit my research team could not have undertaken the x-raying of several hundred coal miners without such an arrangement. And John Craw,[29] the haematite mine's MO, could not have been more helpful in offering assistance. Finally, I arranged for the Unit's dust team to visit the mine and work out the best dust sampling procedure. With their hand pumps they were to provide more accurate assessments of dust levels.

Watson, the head of the dust team, and John Gilson and I returned a while later to finalise dust sampling arrangements with the colliery manager who was remarkably helpful, but during our meeting with him a Telex message came through, although it wasn't called Telex then, saying that Drs Fletcher and Gilson needed to meet the regional NCB chairman urgently at his Newcastle office. So we drove over right away.

He was not in a welcoming mood, protesting that he had not given permission for us to visit the mine and had no intention of allowing us to go ahead with a survey of miners' health. X-rays of miners were out of the question. Such a survey would cause major disruption and create anxiety in the workforce, was the line he took. And he was adamant that we were not to go ahead. I just listened, but when my turn came I simply said "Well, you had better explain to the miners and the Union why we can't carry out this survey". It was a quietly delivered recommendation, but struck home and left him sitting silent for a while considering options. He then backed down and said "Alright, you go ahead, but we'll have to impose conditions". These were that all x-rays of miners should be put into secure storage and the findings only ever published with the approval of the NCB.

With this agreement the way cleared, with a May 1949 date set for the survey. I asked Archie Cochrane to prepare a questionnaire to collect data on each miner's experience of chest disease: about coughs, colds, sputum production, breathlessness and other symptoms. To this he innovatively added questions on smoking history, which was probably the first time this had been done in any British survey.

Although John Gilson took charge of the Haig Colliery survey he was wonderfully assisted by Archie, who worked wonders in achieving a response rate of more than ninety per cent of miners volunteering to be x-rayed. Although the NUM recommended volunteering, it was Archie's beavering-away getting them to attend that secured this remarkable response. He was fanatical in efforts to achieve high response rates, always aiming for a hundred per cent. But the questionnaire that he had devised had less success.

It was administered by Gilson, Cochrane and two other clinical colleagues in one-to-one interviews with miners, but the way in which the questions were asked by different interviewers led to inconsistencies in answering, which came across clearly when their batches of questionnaires were scored. We were shocked by how far interviewing style influenced answers. We had vastly reduced observer error in reading x-rays, but an equivalent problem had raised its head in our questionnaire method. We threw away the results on that occasion, but for later surveys developed a more standardised way of asking questions.

The survey team emerged from Whitehaven with results that we had expected (of high dust levels and low disease incidence) and so we learnt little, but it was a good trial-run and led to improvements in the way we conducted the next survey, which was a comparative one in West Wales at a high dust anthracite mine with high pneumoconiosis incidence. On that occasion arrangements went smoothly because National Coal Board approval of what we were doing had then reached all corners of the industry and good relationships already existed with Coal Board Staff in Wales.

Archie Cochrane took charge of this second survey and achieved a higher response rate than in the first, which provided our first comprehensive view of pneumoconiosis incidence in a high-dust Welsh anthracite mine. And standardised questionnaire interviews provided more reliable data on coughing, sputum production and breathlessness, also strong indications that smoking played no part in pneumoconiosis development.

Soon afterwards, Archie took the team to survey the Bank Hall Colliery at Burnley in Lancashire, where dust levels were high and pneumoconiosis incidence low. Our objective was to explain this situation, with hopes that it would clarify ways of reducing disease incidence in high-dust, high-disease mines.

While arrangements for this third survey went smoothly, a recently acquired mobile x-ray unit (a converted army vehicle) gave us technical problems. It arrived only a day or two before the survey began and was not adequately tried and tested, resulting in a fairly high recall rate of miners needing re-x-raying. But Archie's excellence in getting men to attend transcended this and response rates were higher than before, reaching the ninety-five per cent mark. But while dust levels were carefully recorded and disease levels fastidiously charted radiographically, the team emerged without major revelations. The most fascinating finding came in follow-up studies showing that the pit's relatively small number of pneumoconiosis cases progressed at an unusually fast rate, which was quite a puzzle.

The team came back to South Wales, to the Wattstown Colliery in the Rhondda Fach (the Little Rhondda) for its fourth survey, where again we acquired relevant statistics on dust concentrations and pneumoconiosis incidence. The survey had the advantages of providing follow-up data on men surveyed in the earlier MRC study by Hart and Aslett and whose x-ray data was available. A shortcoming was that men who had been certified had left the mine and were outside the scope of the survey. I think that this lamentable shortfall in data led to Archie Cochrane's fervent commitment to fully inclusive follow-up. At Wattstown he achieved almost a one hundred per cent response rate and belief that he could conduct surveys with the kind of precision possible in laboratory studies. Occasionally, he talked of wanting to survey populations as well as he had been able to monitor ones in which he had been captive "in barbed wire cages", as a prisoner of war doctor. He came up with the concept of studying large, defined populations.

Wattstown was the last in our first series of surveys. Unfortunately, they had not done more than reinforce early views that pneumoconiosis risk depended on the type and amounts of dusts inhaled. Some dusts had better accumulation rates in lungs, but high levels of exposure to ones of lesser hazard could result in pneumoconiosis. Reducing the incidence of this disease seemed to lie in better dust management: finding out what were critical levels of exposure to various dusts and ways of preventing them.

When Archie Cochrane began taking a keener interest in dust sampling and urging improvements he clashed with Watson (the physicist leading the dust team) at some point, and one night arrived at my home quite late insisting rather passionately that Watson be sacked. It was a difficult situation, but Archie pressed for this and in the end I arranged a dismissal package for Watson. I was unhappy about this, but did not want to risk losing Cochrane, who was a much greater asset to the Unit.

Another valued member of the Unit who I have not yet mentioned was Bill Clarke, the senior radiographer, who gave exceptional service, often under pressure during pit surveys. He had replaced John Pierce, who had consistently produced high quality x-ray film in years before the surveys began, but never quite fitted into the research team. And there was Stan Roach, an engineer we employed to assist with pit survey arrangements and who, with Peter Oldham, eventually came up with a rather good way of assessing the dust intake of individual miners that we called the "random collier method". In this, a randomly selected coal-face worker was followed through his shift by a member of our survey team who held a portable dust meter close to him at all times (within about two feet of him). And on each shift throughout a survey a different miner was followed to provide a representative assessment of dust inhalation. This sampling became so good that we began demonstrating the close quantitative relationship that existed between dust exposure and disease levels, which vastly strengthened our recommendations to the NCB on dust management and minimising risk.

The main outcome of our first short series of pit surveys was refinement of methods. And in the physiology laboratory parallel progress was made in studies of breathing impairment in certified miners through innovative developments in lung function testing. Initially Philip Hugh-Jones and John Gilson had used standard laboratory spirometers to measure maximum lung capacity: the volume of a man's deepest breath, but the results were not as sensitive or repeatable as required and so they had thought again and had the idea of measuring forced expiratory volume instead (the speed at which a maximum breath could be expelled). And after devising the right apparatus with the lowest possible resistance to air expulsion, which they did brilliantly, the results had begun revealing a quantitative relationship between disease and decline in lung function, but a complex one in which age and a number of other factors needed taking into account. Hugh-Jones and Gilson have not had the credit they deserve for their pioneering development of forced expiratory volume (FEV) measurement, which considerably advanced respiratory physiology.

Initially they had strong criticism from the leading British expert in respiratory physiology, Professor Ronald Christie at St Bartholomew's Hospital (London), who regarded their attention to FEV as misdirected. This was another example of a leading expert being completely wrong. Forced expiratory flow measurement has become one of the most valuable ways of assessing obstructive lung changes. And the apparatus that Hugh-Jones and Gilson devised was portable enough to be used wherever our surveys went. However, their relationships with

Christie's department remained strong, through close links that they had formed with Patrick Lawther and David Bates.[30]

The advances made in lung function assessment provided a far more accurate classification of disability than our x-ray categories had. Now we could distinguish different levels of disability in men with the same radiographic shadows of pneumoconiosis and formerly categorised together. And age-group studies showed the impact of age on disability levels. Younger men in higher categories of pneumoconiosis could be far less disabled than seniors in lower ones.

The Hugh-Jones and Gilson team was strengthened by input from Martin Wright and Owen Wade,[31] a young research assistant who joined them in 1948. Martin Wright's brilliance as an inventor eventually resulted in the peak flow meter (in the mid-1950s), which is now widely used all over the world and its low-cost mini-version used by hundreds of thousands of asthma sufferers for routine monitoring of bronchial obstruction. The physiology laboratory buzzed with the enthusiasm of this team.

And, wearing his pathologist's hat, Martin Wright was trying to fathom developmental aspects of pneumoconiosis, using experimental animals that were exposed to dust levels typical of the worst pits. For this they were housed in dust-flow chambers that he devised. Post mortem investigations then looked into their dust accumulation.

All teams at the Unit were ardently involved in unravelling aspects of a poorly understood disease. And we were building international links across the field of industrial chest disease. This included attending conferences on the Continent and later making visits to Australia and the USA, where I promoted our radiographic classification of stages of pneumoconiosis and PMF.

Archie Cochrane accompanied me to industrial health conferences in Belgium, France and Germany. His knowledge of European languages made him the ideal colleague to take, although he had strong initial reservations about returning to Germany where he had spent hellish years as a prisoner of war medical officer. His worst memories of these trips turned out to be of times when my blood sugar dipped and I became confused and irritable and he needed to get sugar into me. The first time was on a Channel ferry. The second was during the visit to Germany when I became hypoglycaemic on a rail journey and began tearing up the lecture notes that he had translated into German for me. He was good at spotting the early signs, but for a smaller man it must have been difficult taking control of me when I was far from cooperative. Usually, I managed diabetes rather well, but departures from the norm, such as overseas travel, could catch me out.

Archie Cochrane made good contacts in French industrial medicine and helped establish our radiological classification of pneumoconiosis in France, not least through a persuasive publication of 1949: *Entente radiologique: a step towards international agreement on the classifying of radiographs in pneumoconiosis,*[32] based on discussion with French colleagues.

Then, before 1949 ended, Archie came up with an astounding research proposal. I will never forget the moment (actually in autumn 1949) that he came into my office and put on my desk the one-page protocol on how to discover whether or not TB infection was involved in turning pneumoconiosis into grimly disabling PMF. He called it "The Two Valleys Scheme".

This was because it involved removing all the infectious TB from one of two comparable Welsh mining valleys and then carefully tracking the numbers of new cases of PMF. The other valley would be used merely as a control against which to compare changes in the first one. If TB was an aetiological factor, as we all believed, then few new cases of PMF should arise once infective TB had been removed from that valley.

I read these plans with amazement at their brilliance and audacity. The scheme involved far larger surveys than we had ever contemplated. In the "test valley" from which

TB was to be removed the target population to be surveyed (x-rayed and interviewed) was nearly 20,000 (19,200). Then in the "control valley" all miners and ex-miners, almost 3,000 (2,700) of them, required x-raying and interviewing to acquire medical histories. All this meant considerable extra effort by many of the Unit's staff, as well as input by local health agencies, but we were all quickly bowled over by the proposal and committed to the Two Valleys Scheme.

The valleys that Archie had selected were the Rhondda Fach and Aberdare Valleys, which were remarkably comparable. Each had similar numbers of mining communities, collieries and miners who worked the same type of coal. And although not many miles apart, they were fairly insular.

I was the chief negotiator with the various organisations we needed to support the project, such as the National Coal Board, the Miners' Union and the local authorities and health services that needed to be involved. We could not get far without NCB and NUM approval or without colossal support from the regional mass radiography service in coping with the vast numbers of x-rays to be taken (more than 16,000 in the first phase of the survey). And we needed assistance from the local tuberculosis service in isolating cases of infective TB, as well as assistance in immunising all vulnerable groups with BCG vaccine.

By January 1950 all this support had been secured and we went ahead with promotional talks in the Rhondda Fach preparing the way for the high response rate required.

At the same time I had begun thinking about my future career. I had recently read one or two articles from the USA on respiratory physiology and been shocked by how far I had been left behind. Alarm bells rang in my head, warning of the extent to which I had become an administrator. Also, I was aware of my promise to Lou, to stay in Wales for no longer than five years and that time was running out. And I had begun wanting to be back in academic clinical medicine in London, with thoughts of becoming a professor of medicine, which led me to apply unwisely for the chair of medicine at University College Hospital, London, in February 1950.

I heard that it was being vacated about a fortnight before I was due to fly to Australia to promote the Unit's radiographic system of classifying pneumoconiosis at a conference of the International Labour Organisation (ILO).[33] After discussing with John McMichael my prospects of being considered for the UCH chair and having his support, I dashed off an application. How unworthy it was I learnt later from Professor T R Elliot who told me of the selection panel's surprise at its shoddiness. I had never made a formal application for a job before and had merely sent a letter of interest on blue note-pad paper and attached a short, self-typed page outlining my experience. Even worse was the extent to which I had underestimated the competition for such a post, which went to one of UCH's brightest ever physicians, Max Rosenheim.[34] Even a fully detailed CV from me would not have come close to his. He would have been the automatic choice of any sane appointments panel.

The success of my trip to Australia (from mid-February-mid-March 1950) partly eased my disappointment. It had achieved International Labour Organisation backing for the radiographic classification of stages of pneumoconiosis that my team had developed. And before I left the ILO Conference at Sydney there were plans for the Organisation to begin distributing sets of demonstration x-rays internationally. This was step one towards the ILO System of Classification that John Gilson would refine later in the 1950s. The outcome fully justified my long journey, which was not plain sailing for a diabetic at that time. On long flights I had to check my urine for sugar in cramped aeroplane lavatories where I had to light a small spirit burner to boil up the Fehling's test solution. It wouldn't be allowed nowadays, but now there are easy-to-use blood-glucose test strips.

I returned from Australia by the American route, stopping off at San Francisco to discuss our x-ray classification system with the Yarashami Group of consultants, which had been looking at a specimen set of radiographs that we had sent them. I also saw Garland, a leading radiologist who had visited my Unit in 1949 and become a friend. Then on this first USA visit I had an opportunity to discuss a set of x-ray plates with Philadelphia's chief industrial radiologist, Dr Prendergast, who classified category 1 and 2 plates as normal, failing initially to appreciate the fine detail.

A final stop-over on this trip was at Toronto, to meet Charles Best, the legendary co-discoverer of insulin as a treatment for diabetes. That had been back in 1921 while he was still a medical student, but drawn into assisting Frederick Banting in this epic research. Best had known and admired my father and invited me to stay at the University Club of Toronto. He had been the university's professor of physiology for about 20 years. In correspondence he had invited me to give a lecture to the lay-diabetic association of Toronto on my world travels as a diabetic. I was surprised by how formal an occasion this was and the very large audience. The previous lecture, a month earlier, had been given by the renowned Boston diabetes specialist, Jocelyn, who back in the 1920s had been among early users of insulin. His talk had emphasised the need for fastidious dietary control and strict attention to insulin use, which my talk largely contradicted. I believed in sensible flexibility and not being over-concerned with routine. I emphasised that it was possible to live a fairly free, unrestricted life, without the burden of meticulous dietary arrangements. I pointed out that during my travels mealtimes, foods and numbers of meals per day inevitably varied, but that by testing blood glucose levels fairly frequently I managed to adjust my insulin use accordingly and keep blood sugar levels from straying out of normal limits. I wanted diabetics to feel far less restricted in lifestyle. My message was "Be sensible, be adaptable". And the audience was so delighted with the talk that I was asked if I would record it on a long playing gramophone record for the Canadian Diabetic Association to distribute. I had only used rough notes, but mulled over them carefully and then went to Charles Best's house on my final day in Toronto where a man with a recording machine was waiting and I put on record my views. The long-playing record that resulted was widely used in Canadian diabetic circles. I thoroughly enjoyed my stay with Best and we remained in friendly contact until the last year of his life (1978, aged 79).

When I got back to Cardiff (late in March 1950) final preparations for part 1 of Archie Cochrane's Two Valleys Scheme were under way. During summer months there was a steady increase in publicity promoting the project. Local media coverage was generous, backed by posters and leaflets. By September, Archie and his team and a range of collaborators were ready to go ahead with their mammoth chest x-ray survey of the adult population of the Rhondda Fach. Cases of infectious TB needed finding and isolating. Detailed records were needed of pneumoconiosis and PMF in the valley's mining communities. Time would tell whether or not local reductions in TB infection reduced PMF incidence; whether TB had a major part in transforming pneumoconiosis into the industry's most disabling disease.

In October I spoke on radio about the diseases we were investigating and research in progress. The BBC invited me to speak for fifteen minutes after the 9 o'clock Sunday evening news, in a prime slot reserved for talks of national importance. Under the title *Fighting the Modern Black Death* I told of the scale of the problem and the importance of solving it for a major industry. That was my first experience of talking live to a national audience and what I said was published in *The Listener* a week later.[35] (A year later I wrote an article on similar lines for *The Municipal Journal*.[36])

Part 1 of Archie's Two Valleys Scheme stretched over eight months, including a harsh winter with lots of snow. His team and collaborators worked valiantly and were justly rewarded by the results. By April 1951 we had a detailed picture of pneumoconiosis and PMF in the Rhondda Fach, plus the success of isolating much of the infectious TB found in the population. At last we had a basis for detecting whether this changed miners' risks of PMF; whether TB was a causal factor.

Almost 90 per cent of the adult population (of 19,200) had been chest x-rayed, and the percentage for miners and ex-miners was more impressive. 98 per cent of almost 3,000 of them had had x-rays and medical histories taken. Achieving such response rates rewarded the beavering-away of members of Archie's team, who had made more than 20,000 home visits to remind and encourage individuals to participate. Often they worked ten-hour days. Some homes had needed visiting several times. Occasionally, I was asked to encourage the most resistant individuals. Archie thought that I might be more persuasive, but my success rate was lamentably low.

The Welsh Miniature Mass Radiography Service played a major part in this vast x-ray survey. While Archie and his team took the PRU's mobile x-ray unit to collieries of the Rhondda Fach and chest x-rayed miners and ex-miners, chest x-rays of the rest of the adult population were undertaken by this mass radiography service, which toured the small towns of the valley and operated in public halls and chapel vestries. A surprise to its radiographers was the fairly large number of women with undiagnosed TB. As Archie had arranged, all infectious cases were moved to isolation wards that had been prepared at the local Tyntyla Hospital. The mass radiography service was led by Dr Francis Jarman, who cooperated well without ever getting on well with Archie.

Soon after the survey of the Rhondda Fach was completed, Archie took our mobile x-ray unit to the Aberdare Valley and with about seven or eight colleagues set about x-raying all the miners and ex-miners living there. Again, response rates were impressive at 98 per cent of the target population (of around 2,700) and chest disease histories of all these men were amassed.

With virtually all cases of pneumoconiosis and PMF charted in these two populations of miners, we had to wait for a year or two (2 years) for Archie's planned follow-up surveys to show whether or not TB transformed pneumoconiosis into PMF. Answering this question held the key to massive advances in prevention.

What quickly became clear was that all the data we had collected on the well defined mining communities of the Rhondda Fach made it a unique reference population for further health surveys. Nowhere had more data been collected on the health of a population. And we had made the most accurate assessment of the amount of tuberculosis in a community ever achieved.

It was in using the x-ray records of this population that we helped Anthony Caplan, a physician on the pneumoconiosis certification panel, to confirm his view that men with a particular kind of chest x-ray shadowing were likely to have rheumatoid arthritis. We had all seen these strange little sacular shadows (0.5-2.0 cm in diameter) from time to time in pneumoconiosis cases and called them the fingerprint pattern. But unlike Caplan we had not made the connection with rheumatoid arthritis. After just a year on the certification panel his sharp mind had recognised what hundreds of observers had missed.[37]

I remember him coming to the Unit and mentioning his observation, then Archie and colleagues checking through all the Rhondda Fach x-rays for ones with the fingerprint pattern. When these cases were followed-up about seventy per cent of the men were found to have rheumatoid arthritis. This association of pneumoconiosis and rheumatoid arthritis became known as Caplan's syndrome. A few years later Caplan became the principal medical officer of the Ministry of Pensions, a highly qualified physician who had missed-out on a consultant's post in the new NHS by returning too late from a job in India as a medical officer in the Kolar Goldfields.

A major concern of 1951 was the limited progress we had made in understanding the relationship between dust and pneumoconiosis development. We knew the relative degrees of risk existing across a range of mines, which had assisted recommendations on the damping-down of dust in them all, but I felt that we needed more accurate soundings on the quantitative relationship between dust exposure and disease. I felt that we should be specifying safe levels of exposure and with my advisory team of senior colleagues formulated prospective studies of dust exposure and disease incidence in about 20 representative pits, using the random collier method of sampling and annual x-ray examination of all their miners for several years. This was a considerable undertaking, but the NCB and NUM recognised the need to specify safety levels.

Although it is impossible to have dust-free and entirely safe coal workings, we wanted to specify the safest achievable levels of dust exposure.

We were well into discussing the logistics of such a large project (with the NCB, NUM and MRC) when I went to Belfast in June 1951 as a candidate short-listed for the chair of medicine at Queen's University. I had been encouraged to apply for the job by a former Bart's medical school colleague, Harold Rodgers, who had become the professor of surgery at Belfast. I took Lou with me and we could not have had a more enjoyable visit, travelling over to Northern Ireland on my birthday (5th June) and having two days of the province's brightest weather for our stay and being shown around by the Vice-Chancellor, the distinguished botanist Eric Ashby, with whom we stayed. Unfortunately, we realised how much further away from family and friends we would be in Belfast, which sadly prevented me from taking the job when it was offered. After one unsuccessful bid for a chair that I would have taken, I now had the offer of an unacceptable one.

With no other chairs of medicine on the horizon, I was rescued from uncertainties of when the next chance would arise by an invitation to take a job back at the Hammersmith Postgraduate Medical School. This came just a few weeks after the Belfast visit, while I was holidaying with my family on the Isle of Wight in August 1951. A letter from John McMichael suggested that I might like to take the job of senior lecturer in chest diseases that was coming up in his department. John Crofton was leaving to become the professor of TB and chest medicine at Edinburgh. This invitation seemed a lifeline and I was not long in accepting it. The chance to get back to London and work again with John McMichael felt irresistible. And the prospect of living in Richmond-on-Thames again delighted Lou.

By the time that I returned to Cardiff from the summer vacation I had accepted the post and at a meeting of all my staff informed them of this. My plans to move on had been kept rather private and this was a shock to them. I suspect that most were surprised by what must have seemed a downward step for me (relinquishing the leadership of a major research unit to become a senior lecturer). At that time they probably appreciated this more than I did. I was too intent on re-establishing myself in academic clinical medicine in London. But John McMichael had kindly given me nine months in which to wind-down what I was doing in Wales alongside preparing for my new job.

On my recommendation, the MRC appointed John Gilson as my successor. He was the right man for the job: sound as a rock administratively and technically impressive. Philip Hugh-Jones, his senior at the Unit, who had become one of our closest family friends, had recently taken a job in Jamaica and so there was no awkwardness in wanting John to take over.

My concluding months in Wales coincided with pressure from the National Coal Board to take over the large-scale dust-exposure studies at 20 collieries that we had planned. By 1951 the NCB was getting into its stride for such research and its new chief medical officer, John Rogan,[38] was adamant that he should be in charge of the project. He was among the most difficult men I have met, with little respect for views other than his own. I was surprised when he once asked my advice. But logic was on his side and I felt that the NCB should take charge of investigating coal mining disease. John Gilson shared that view, although he changed it later when Rogan and his

NCB colleagues began publishing on pneumoconiosis research without ever acknowledging the techniques they had inherited from us and used in acquiring their results. Only Archie Cochrane objected to the Coal Board taking over a project that he felt better able to administer.

Although we remain good friends, Archie has never quite forgiven me for leaving the Unit when I did and conceding major research to the NCB, although ultimately his own career benefited from this. Unhappy with changes he later moved to a Chair in the Cardiff medical school and soon had opportunities to extend his research interests as the developer of a new epidemiology unit for the MRC, with increasing influence in the field of clinical trials.[39]

I left Cardiff in July 1952 with a curious blend of sadness and relief. (80 members of current and former MRC Unit staff had contributed to a generous leaving present.) It was good to be returning to clinical medicine in a major London hospital and Lou had found us another fine house in Richmond, which we loved. But I had become deeply and emotionally involved in the project of making mining safer from pneumoconiosis and felt torn to be leaving it, although I think the right time had been reached. The job had been far more fulfilling than I ever imagined it would be.

The chance to build a major MRC research unit had proved an astounding privilege. The colleagues who had joined me had improved x-ray diagnosis of the disease, disability appraisal and the rehabilitation and re-employment prospects of many thousands of coal miners. Our chest x-ray classification of stages of the disease had become internationally accepted and we had taken studies of the relationship between dust exposure and disease development to new levels, with clear guidelines on dust reduction. A major advance on the 1930s MRC study of the disease had been in showing that simple pneumoconiosis was not usually disabling. While we had emphasised the need for men to cease working underground on reaching category 2 of our revised chest x-ray classification, beyond which the risks of highly disabling progressive massive fibrosis arose, we had shown that compensation should be for loss of their original jobs, not because they were disabled. This had greatly changed the prospects of them being re-employed and not left prematurely redundant as before. We had also shown that progressive massive fibrosis was not related to dust accumulation.

Measurement of breathing impairment had also been advanced by the Unit's respiratory physiologists who had improved spirometer design and shown the advantages of FEV assessment. They had taken respiratory physiology to new levels. And I could not have been happier with the way in which the links established with mining communities had shown miners how much their health mattered.

Lou was overjoyed when the furniture vans removed our furnishings from Hickley Lodge and we drove to London. She was not sorry to say good-bye to this large ugly house which had been too expensive to run and kept us feeling the poor relations of both our families. Susanna, then 7, was sad to leave the little nearby school and the garden she loved. Mark had already been uprooted at 9 and begun at a Wiltshire preparatory school. Caroline was just 3 and largely unaware of the uprooting. Her years at Hickley Lodge had been plagued by asthma and eczema.

For me, a remarkable excursion into industrial medicine had ended.

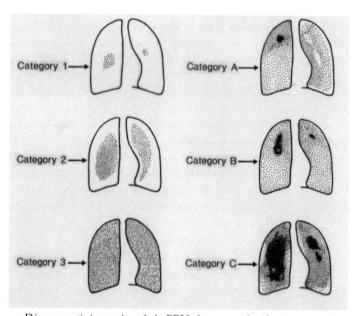

Diagrammatic impression of the PRU chest x-ray classification stages of pneumoconiosis (1, 2 and 3) and progressive massive fibrosis (A, B and C)

A typical South Wales coal mining valley town

The new PRU laboratory building, Llandough Hospital, 1949

(Photograph provided by Cardiff University Library, Cochrane Archive, University Hospital Llandough)

PRU mobile x-ray unit vans and tents at the Tylorstown pithead, Rhondda Valley, Mid Glamorgan, in 1950, during the initial "Two Valleys" survey of TB and pneumoconiosis incidence.

Archie Cochrane's PRU team with National Coal Board and National Union of Mineworkers officials involved in the 1949 survey of coal miners' health at Bank Hall Colliery, Burnley, Lancashire. (Archie is third from the left on the front row.)

Chapter 6
The worst of times: a difficult return to clinical medicine including severe depression and tuberculosis

Inevitably, my return to London and academic clinical medicine was stressful. I had not accounted for the difficult acclimatisation of moving from leading a large research unit to the lowlier role of senior lecturer in respiratory medicine. And I had under-estimated the challenge of being a chest physician. Working alongside Guy Scadding,[1] a leading chest specialist, showed me just how far I fell short. The specialty had advanced considerably since my days as a house physician and the registrars assisting me knew far more than I did. A more embarrassing start would have been difficult to envisage. I had transferred from a position in which I had a national reputation to a lesser one in which I felt unsatisfactory.

Even before going to South Wales my specialist interests had been in gastroenterology and my recent experience of chest disease had been largely confined to pneumoconiosis. I knew far too little of tuberculosis, the most common problem, and developments in its treatment.

If I had been wise, I would have arranged an updating attachment to the Brompton Hospital for three or four months before joining the staff of the Hammersmith. The Brompton was the leading chest disease centre and I had friends there, including Guy Scadding. But the nine months that John McMichael had allowed for winding-down in Wales and preparing for my new appointment had largely gone on the former.

An additional pressure at the Hammersmith was John McMichael's expectation that I would continue with the kind of high-powered physiological research that my predecessor, John Crofton, had established. But I was not a clinical physiologist and this left me urgently considering research alternatives.

In contrast to my early anguished months at the Hammersmith, Lou could not have been more happily engaged in setting up home back in Richmond-on-Thames. With her flair for finding the right house, we had a delightful property on the Green,[2] not far from where we had loved living before.

My despair at moving to Hammersmith Hospital and the Postgraduate Medical School was eased at the beginning of 1953 by the distraction of presenting a short series of five television programmes on post-war advances in medicine for the BBC. On the recommendation of John Agate, a young doctor in occupational medicine who had visited the Unit in Wales, I had been checked-out and chosen to front the series. Agate had strong acting and broadcasting links and had been asked by producer Andrew Miller Jones about possible presenters of the series and suggested me.

The programmes of this trial series on *Matters of Medicine* were broadcast live from Alexandra Palace. Andrew Miller Jones's emphasis was that they needed to have the popular appeal of a main feature article in the *Daily Mirror*. And the first programme fulfilled that requirement brilliantly. It was on pain and pain relief and included reference to the relief that hypnosis could achieve. It concluded with an interview with Odette Churchill, a famous allied agent in the second world war, who told me how she had evaded pain while being severely tortured by SS interrogators. While her fingernails were being extracted she had been able to detach her mind from what was happening and let it soar like a little bird through a small open window and fly around outside. This state of hysteria had rendered her immune to pain. She had this amazing capacity of detaching herself from reality.

In one of the programmes on dust and dust diseases, which appeared the least interesting, I had the opportunity to speak dramatically of the diseases of miners and the

114

research of my former unit, which somehow kept viewing figures higher than expected. As a programme presenter I was able to act as the kind of doctor I would like to have been.

At that time only the BBC had a TV channel and most of its programmes were live and all in black and white. Colour was still a decade away. I presented programmes sitting at a desk which had a six-by-five inch slot through which I could view a small monitor. The pre-recording of programmes followed two or three years later, but I preferred the challenge of broadcasting live. I enjoyed the thrill of talking directly to the audience and being in charge of the flow of a programme, with the swift adapting this often required.

But after the excitement of presenting this series I descended into depression, increasingly lost in despair about making the wrong career move. I was convinced that I had wrecked my career and that little ahead was worthwhile. Utter worthlessness is what I felt.

Lou was absolutely marvellous. She kept telling me that everything was going to be alright, that I would get over all the despair. They were difficult times for her, the grimmest of our married life.[3] She knew little about depression, but had to endure its bleakness and impact on the family, in which I took little interest.

I spoke little with my children. Thoughts of play were gone. Even the choice of my son's next school I could not have cared less about, although Lou took me to look at one or two (Winchester and Bryanston). And my gardening interests lapsed. Out in the garden, the planes heard overhead just reinforced the bleak outlook that I would never travel again. But for many months I managed to conceal my problems from hospital colleagues, as an actor might.

The first outsider to detect that I had a problem was Erasmus Barlow,[4] a friend and psychiatrist who lived across the Green from our new Richmond house. He talked with Lou and suggested that I see his chief at St Thomas's Hospital, William Sargant,[5] the most progressive force in British psychiatry at that time. He had a reputation for sorting out the misery of many traumatised troops of the 39-45 war by various drug and shock treatments. At the end of the war he had written (with Eliot Slater, the wartime head of psychiatry at St George's Hospital) the leading-edge textbook on physical methods of treatment in psychiatry,[6] based on his use of drugs, leucotomy and insulin shock and electroconvulsive therapy (ECT).

Sargant was renowned for blasting away psychiatric problems by physiological attack. He loathed the slow Freudian analysis routes to relieving misery. I saw him in March 1953, but did not like his insensitive, autocratic approach to my problems and left without making another appointment.

I was rescued from indecision about who to consult next by John McMichael, who shortly afterwards recognised that I had problems and pointed me in the direction of a Jungian psychiatrist he knew in Harley Street (Edward A Bennet), who I rather liked. I began seeing him in April 1953 and he set out to analyse my dreams, but made little progress because I had none to report. I was sleeping only with the aid of sedatives and dreamlessly. When I began having suicidal thoughts he rapidly recommended that I go back to Sargant for help.

I remember several dark days of planning my death. One was my son's birthday in October 1953 when we all went to see the new Walt Disney cartoon film of *Peter Pan* at London's Leicester Square Odeon and I sat planning my suicide, while feeling a curiously detached sympathy for the lovely family I was leaving behind.

Soon afterwards I went with Lou to see Sargant. She disliked him more than I did, especially his brutally cold pronouncement that I needed electroconvulsive therapy, which left us reeling. It was a notorious treatment. The pros and cons of ECT we were left to discuss with our neighbour Erasmus Barlow, who was very positive on likely benefits. And so was my cousin, Richard Acland. He had severe depression soon after his Common Wealth Party[7] had fallen apart at the 1945 General Election, and had come out of it well. So I booked-in for ECT treatment in Sargant's department at St Thomas's.

It was given under a general anaesthetic and I awoke with just a headache, which slowly cleared and left me feeling immensely brighter. Just one treatment had shocked me out of black despair. But then I made the mistake of returning for a consolidating second ECT treatment which had no further benefit and damaged a little of my memory, which has never been particularly good.

Not long after recovering from deep depression, I had the additional pleasure of being created a CBE in recognition of my work on pneumoconiosis. This came with the New Year's Honours List of 1954.

By then, I was back at Hammersmith Hospital intent on making up for lost time, particularly in getting some line of research started. John McMichael had been awaiting this for eighteen months. With my limited research skills I was looking for a broader rather than a narrow, specialised canvas of opportunity. Chronic bronchitis, the most commonplace and long under-researched chest disease, offered this. It had been on my mind since the time of the great London smog of December 1952, when the atmospheric pollution resulted in London's hospitals being deluged to overflowing by severe cases of bronchitis and asthma. At Hammersmith Hospital I had cared for an exceptional number of breathless men and women who were all in a very bad way, victims of the worst air pollution of their lives. Exceptional climatic conditions had trapped the ground-air in a fairly static state collecting all the smoke of London, from industries and many thousands of domestic coal fires, into a dense wet smog, denser than any on record. The horrific statistics of the suffering and fatalities[8] among asthma and bronchitis sufferers had drawn long-overdue attention to these diseases.

Influenced by my pneumoconiosis unit background my initial idea was to research the difference between the bronchi of sufferers and non-sufferers of chronic

117

bronchitis. I had some naïve notion that the mucus-clearing cilia (the motile, microscopic hair-like projections of cells lining the bronchial tubes) of bronchitis sufferers would be performing differently. And I felt that the kind of dust inhalation apparatus that my pneumoconiosis research colleague Martin Wright had invented for testing the effects of dust on laboratory animals' lungs could be adapted for investigations on humans. After discussing my interests he soon produced a dust chamber that I could trial, which I went down to Cardiff to test (at the PRU). From the Hammersmith I took with me a new, fine barium powder that was being used to produce barium meals and which I planned to inhale in Martin's apparatus. The hope was that this opaque powder would then provide x-ray evidence of how the bronchial cilia were functioning. If successful, I could then use this procedure in comparative studies of cilia action in chronic bronchitis sufferers.

I vividly remember the winter's morning at Cardiff in 1954 when we put it to the test. After Martin had cranked up the inhalation machine and achieved a satisfactory level of dust flow, I put my head into the breathing chamber and took a couple of breaths of the dusty air, then straight afterwards had an x-ray film taken of my upper chest and neck region. But the results were not helpful. The x-ray film showed that all the inhaled dust had collected around my vocal cords.

Then came one of the worst moments of my life. While looking at the film I discovered a small round shadow near the apex of the right lung, which looked astoundingly like TB. John Gilson, the director of the Pneumoconiosis Research Unit was called for a second opinion that confirmed mine, and then a larger film was taken, which removed any doubts. It was a bizarre way to discover that I had tuberculosis.

On returning to the Hammersmith I had the laboratory check my sputum for tubercle and when the test proved positive arranged to see my TB specialist colleague, Guy Scadding. I saw him at the Brompton Hospital where he had detailed tomographs and sectional x-rays taken and showed that it was "minimal TB". Following this, I went into a side room on a ward at the Hammersmith for treatment. Once again, I had been blown off course and could not have felt more ill-fated.

Although feeling perfectly well, I had to endure eight or nine weeks of bed-rest, which seemed an eternity. My treatment for TB was just before John Crofton, my predecessor at the Hammersmith, demonstrated at Edinburgh that patients with minimal TB had no need of bed-rest. I was put onto the standard drugs then being used: streptomycin and para-aminosalicylic acid (the combination of antibiotics found most effective and in use since the late 1940s).

I was rescued from boredom in these bed-rest months by reading, knitting and listening to the radio. Medical colleagues of a recently formed London seminar club, the Keppel Club[9] (formed in 1953) at the London School of Hygiene and Tropical Medicine sent me a generous gift of books. I read most of them and at other times knitted and listened to classical music on radio. Knitting I had begun during the war as a contribution to the war effort, producing long sea boot socks for sailors. During this lengthy period in hospital I advanced to doing Fair Isle knitting and produced garments for most of my family. But I became very weak just lying in bed. There is nothing like prolonged bed rest for making you feel ill.

When I came out of hospital I was far weaker than when admitted and the exercise that I began taking was carefully specified, as it was for all patients recovering from TB. Guy Scadding provided the graduated exercise programme that I followed, which began with fifty slow walking paces a day. Regaining physical fitness was a slow process, but towards the end of month two I had strength enough to begin building a concrete-walled sandpit for Caroline, then five.

Susanna (aged 9) was soon to begin at London's Francis Holland School, a private London girls' day school where she had been accepted only after Lou explained that

Canon Francis Holland (1828-1907), the founder, was her great-great uncle. He had been my mother's favourite uncle. Caroline followed her a few years later.

In the final months of recovering from TB I had increasing numbers of visits by colleagues and friends and enjoyed a writing assignment. Also, Lou and I felt better off financially because TB was recognised as an occupational disease of doctors and I received industrial injury benefit in addition to sickness pay. And our subdued lifestyle in this period lowered our spending. Until then, Lou's choice of houses bigger than we could afford had left our finances stretched.

While convalescing I had two visits from Archie Cochrane. Unfortunately his vast two valleys research project in the Rhondda was being undermined by the speed at which TB was disappearing from both valleys. It had set out to solve the great problem of whether or not TB infection had a key role in transforming simple pneumoconiosis into highly disabling PMF, but the recently introduced antibiotic treatment of TB had begun reducing incidence of the disease in both valleys and undermining results and their importance. But Archie had begun looking ahead to using such well researched populations for other health surveys, which of course he brilliantly did over the next thirty years.

A main commitment of this convalescence period was writing a chapter on chest diseases for a new *Textbook of Medicine*, which editor John Richardson[10] had invited me to contribute. This seemed an ideal opportunity to update my knowledge of chest diseases and in preparing the chapter I read all of the latest literature. The Textbook was not a success and a second edition was never a prospect.[11] Richardson's editing had been too uncritical. Some of the chapters were appalling. The one on cardiac disease was so inadequate that I could have done better. My chapter was among the few receiving favourable reviews.

While writing it I took up an invitation to join a recently formed MRC committee on chronic bronchitis that was being chaired by Ronald Christie, my former Bart's professor and leading expert on chest diseases. He asked me to be its secretary and I agreed. This committee was one outcome of the publicity that bronchitis victims had received at the time of the great London smog of 1952. The other was the creation of an MRC air pollution research unit. There were lots of questions to be answered about chronic bronchitis and ways of reducing atmospheric pollution.

I could not have had a more enjoyable final fortnight of convalescence than on a short unexpected holiday in Italy that we were encouraged to take by my Cambridge Trinity Group friend Humphrey Whitbread, who sent us a £100 cheque to ensure that we did. In June 1954 Lou and I went to Venice for almost a week and then to the lovely town of Urbino and finally Florence, before flying home feeling wonderfully relaxed.

Not long after returning to my job at Hammersmith Hospital towards the end of 1954, I attended my first meeting of the MRC committee on chronic bronchitis on which were good friends Richard Doll and John Gilson, also Donald Reid,[12] the reader in epidemiology (and later professor) at the London School of Hygiene and Tropical Medicine, who was to become a generous research ally.

As I resumed work again, as senior lecturer in chest diseases at the Hammersmith, I found that all the reading undertaken before writing my chapter for the Richardson edited *Encyclopaedia of Medical Practice* had up-dated me onto level terms with the best of my registrars. So, having chest disease actually helped my career in chest medicine.

I had gone through two dismal years, but felt back on track again.

Chapter 7
Pioneering bronchitis studies, becoming Britain's first TV doctor and not becoming the professor of medicine at Bart's

My earliest 1955 recollections are of interviewing Sir Alexander Fleming in a live TV broadcast (on 12 January) and soon afterwards applying for the chair of medicine at Bart's, where I had trained. I had only just got back into my stride at Hammersmith Hospital, but could not resist applying for the Bart's job, which had long been a leading ambition.

Ronald Christie, who chaired the MRC committee on bronchitis on which I sat, was leaving it to take a leading medical post in Quebec (as chief physician at Montreal's main hospital and the McGill University medical school)

I began preparing an application for his Bart's chair soon after the interview with Fleming for the BBC Panorama programme (the seventh) which went out live at that time on the only British TV channel. I loved the challenge of live broadcasting to a large national audience with its need for fluent presenting skills and where I had the benefit of amateur acting experience.

I had high hopes of getting the Bart's job. Several distinguished London University deans of medicine supported my application. But after being short-listed and interviewed I had the bitter disappointment of not being selected, disappointment that lingered for many years. Bart's preferred an internal candidate, Eric Scowen,[1] who had been on the staff since my student days and made important post-war contributions to the medical school as well as setting up an endocrinology research unit. The strong internal links that this fine physician had built ensured his selection.

But his appointment was not ratified by London University (which funded the Bart's chair of medicine).

From inner sources I heard that London University had pushed for my appointment on account of the eminent support that I had received, but with neither side backing down stalemate resulted and an appointment to the chair was not made. Instead, Bart's appointed Scowen as the director of its medical unit, which the Bart's board of trustees cleverly chose to rename as the professorial medical unit. As the professor-in-waiting, Scowen had rather a long wait of six years before being appointed to the chair. This nonsensical situation fitted the difficult relationship then existing between London University and Bart's which had become rather bitter in the late 1940s when Bart's had been forced by the University into accepting women students.

It is possible that a lecture that I had given at Bart's two or three years earlier had counted against me. Several senior consultants had been annoyed by references made to the worst of my training there, just as backs had been put up by my student days candid camera pranks.

Not getting the Bart's chair left me to continue developing my career in chest medicine at the Hammersmith, including research to clarify the character of chronic bronchitis, which was far from clearly defined. With TB virtually vanquished by antibiotics, the long under-researched chronic obstructive pulmonary diseases, bronchitis and emphysema, had at last begun attracting the attention they merited. With their symptoms puzzlingly overlapping there was much unravelling to do and my sights were set on accurately defining chronic bronchitis, a disease afflicting hundreds of thousands of Britons and accounting for a majority of GP consultations and colossal national burden of workdays lost.

By the time that Mark went to Eton in September 1955 I had established a bronchitis clinic at Hammersmith Hospital to increase data collection and towards the end of that year had major help in developing physiological and pathological investigations when former pneumo-coniosis research unit colleague and friend Philip Hugh-Jones became a fellow specialist at the hospital. He had recently returned from working in Jamaica. In addition to his clinical competence he knew far more about respiratory physiology than me and provided laboratory expertise that I lacked. Also, I had strong support from an impressive senior registrar, Peter Elmes,[2] who was later a professor at Belfast. We undertook several controlled trials of antibiotics in the treatment of chronic bronchitis, but found them ineffective.

But hospital investigations were of advanced cases of chronic bronchitis and I felt the need to investigate the disease's early stages, to know more of its origins. In my work in South Wales, epidemiological surveys had unravelled the natural history of miners' pneumoconiosis and my thoughts turned to similar surveys of chronic bronchitis. But they were not to be popular with my chief, John McMichael, who regarded epidemiological surveys as "soft research". His priority would have been for me to advance the clinical research reputation of his department. But a *Lancet* article that I had recently read reinforced my commitment to an epidemiological approach. In it, Sir James Spence, the professor of paediatrics at Newcastle, denounced the disproportionate attention given to advanced stages of disease at the expense of researching earlier stages and ways of preventing their progress. That publication (of 1950)[3] had considerable impact on me at a critical time.

And I had exceptional encouragement from Donald Reid, a colleague on the MRC Committee on Chronic Bronchitis who was the reader in epidemiology at the London School of Hygiene and Tropical Medicine (LSHTM). Donald helped with the planning of a first survey, for which he generously gave me access to the large population of London post office employees that he already had under surveillance. This saved me from the considerable problems of developing major survey connections. Our plan was to ask several hundreds of post office employees to complete a questionnaire on their experiences of chest illness. Among a large number of them in the selected 40-60 age-range examples of chronic bronchitis would be fairly prevalent, as it was the disease most common in urban working populations, with cough and sputum production its main characteristics. In the early 1950s my colleague Guy Scadding had defined it as a disease principally of "recurrent cough with expectoration".[4]

The questionnaire that we devised asked about fifty questions on chest disease experienced in the last two years. Answers were mainly of the yes-or-no kind on symptoms such as cough, sputum production and breathlessness. In addition we asked about the times of illness, workdays lost and smoking habits. And we were rewarded by masses of data with which to begin assembling a picture of a disease too commonplace to have attracted detailed epidemiological investigation before. We put all the findings onto punch cards that went off for analysis at the London School of Hygiene and Tropical Medicine in the summer of 1957. I still remember the laborious hand-punching of hundreds of punch-cards, the results of which were then scored by mechanical counting machines. Modern electronic computer analysis of data had hardly dawned at that time.

In January 1957 I had been booked to present two programmes in a short BBC TV series of five on psychiatric illness, entitled *The Hurt Mind*, and following the success of these programmes the producer of a newly launched early evening magazine programme *Tonight* (launched in February 1957) began calling on me to speak on medical issues making the headlines. On average I appeared about twice a month and astoundingly began being called the *Tonight Doctor*. Often I had to respond to emerging medical news at short notice, as on the day when it was announced that Prince Charles was to have his tonsils out. I was telephoned in mid-afternoon while taking an out-patients' clinic and asked to prepare a piece on tonsillectomy for that evening's programme at about 6.30pm. With tonsillectomy becoming controversial it needed cautious preparation.

Then in the summer of 1957 I was asked by Mary Adams, the head of science and features programmes at BBC TV, to be the presenter of a major series of ten programmes being planned for 1958. The producer, Bill Duncalf, had recently had excellent viewing figures for a short series of three programmes (*Thursday Clinic*) on specialist care at St Mary's Hospital, Paddington, but his concentration on just one hospital had brought criticism. In response, his new series aimed to show specialist expertise in a range of hospitals. Each of the BBC's five administrative regions had been asked to nominate two of them. A couple of months into planning this new series, Bill Duncalf and Mary Adams, came up with the series title *Your Life in Their Hands*.

1957 concluded with a two month lecture tour of the United States and Canada. Arrangements had been developing for almost a year, since I received an invitation to give the main annual lecture of the California Medical Society at the end of September '57. It came from Harry Garland, the San Francisco radiologist who had become a friend since visiting the MRC Pneumoconiosis Research Unit in 1949. I had visited him on my 1950 US trip. He sent the invitation soon after becoming the president of the California Medical Society late in 1956, offering a colossal fee of fifteen hundred dollars, which was enough to take Lou and me over for an extended visit. And when other US contacts heard of this there were further invitations that snowballed into a two month tour, including engagements in Canada. To meet different requests, I prepared lectures on chronic bronchitis, pneumoconiosis and observer error.

We set out on 25 September on a trip that took us to New York, San Francisco, Los Angeles, Salt Lake City, Denver, Pittsburgh, Cincinatti, Boston, Montreal, and back to New York from where Lou returned to England early in November, after which I went on to Philadelphia, Cleveland, Charleston, the South Carolina Coalfields, Kentucky, Washington and finally New York again on a second round of engagements. I had packed in so many that I was close to exhaustion by the time that I flew back to England on 11 December.

I had given about a dozen lectures, visited more than twenty hospitals and several medical schools, talked with a large number of respiratory physicians, visited several mines and mining areas to discuss mining diseases with local specialists and contributed to two conferences.

My highly paid lecture to the California Medical Society was the main disappointment. It was given in the palatial ballroom of San Francisco's St. Francis Hotel to a black-tie audience of about 200 and should have been on chronic bronchitis, but with the results of my survey not available at the time of flying out I had hastily reinforced it, while travelling, with a section on pneumoconiosis. Few lectures ever had a worse start, with projection problems and the lecturer's dais rising alarmingly like a cinema organ when I pressed the wrong button on the lectern. And interesting the audience in chronic bronchitis was an uphill struggle. Only later did I learn that in America it was generally regarded as nothing more than a component of emphysema. That British and American definitions of chronic obstructive lung diseases were different was an immense surprise. There was much better audience response when I talked on pneumoconiosis because of regional interests in silicosis. Overall, I scored my performance as seven out of ten, but Harry Garland was delighted by the interest generated.

I had a number of curious lecture engagements. My second in Salt Lake City is a good example. The doctor arranging it had booked a vast lecture hall, but advertised poorly, leaving me speaking to an audience of seven.

The golden moment of early weeks was a visit to the Grand Canyon where Lou and I stayed at a Lodge on the rim and at sunrise watched the spectacular early lighting of the canyon.

One of my early hospital visits was to an emphysema clinic at Denver where I spoke with patients about their symptoms and found that more than half of them would have been diagnosed as having chronic bronchitis if examined in Britain. Answers to my questions on sputum production distinguished them from the rest, which was a great surprise to the consultant (Dr Mitchell) who had never considered sputum output relevant.

American physicians regarded chronic bronchitis as nothing more than a minor feature of emphysema. To them it was not a disease in its own right. The coughing was regarded as trivial as smoker's cough. In British medicine, chronic bronchitis was the commonly diagnosed disease, with emphysema regarded as the later form of it.

By the time that I lectured on chronic bronchitis at the Harvard Medical School at Cambridge, Massachusetts, at the end of October the results of my questionnaire survey of post office employees had caught up with me and drew considerable interest. While at Harvard I had the privilege of hearing Willie Castle, the legendary discoverer of the cause of pernicious anaemia,[5] talking with medical students. His teaching was superb, impressively drawing students into discussion and providing references to all the publications they needed to read, right down to journal volume and page number. He was about 60 then.

I followed my stay at Harvard with 3 days in Boston where I contributed to a conference on the investigation of chest diseases, after which Lou and I returned to New York for 4 days before her return to England on 8th November. There we were the guests of Bill Briscoe,[6] who had been on the staff of my Unit in Wales, and his wife, who were splendid hosts. Bill was then a professor at Cornell University and still wonderfully idiosyncratic at times. Archie Cochrane remembered him attending a dress ball immaculately attired but wearing Wellington boots. Before Lou's departure we saw a sparkling performance of *My Fair Lady* on Broadway.

I gave two lectures in New York and visited four or five hospitals to meet chest disease specialists, after which I went on to engagements in Philadelphia, Cleveland (Ohio), Charleston, Kentucky and Washington. In Philadelphia I visited several hospitals and enjoyed hearing the Philadelphia Orchestra and a superb performance of the Beethoven violin concerto with the soloist Zino Francescatti. In Cleveland I lectured on observer variation, talked with the State's atmospheric pollution committee and found medical education at Case Western Reserve University the most enlightened of my experience. Lecture engagements at Charleston, Kentucky and Washington followed. And in Washington I received an invitation to talk with the leader of the mighty US Union of Mine Workers (UMW), the industrial colossus John Llewellyn Lewis whose vast office must have been twenty metres long. I had visited hospitals in the Carolina coalfields that he had been influential in founding by pressurising funding from the mine owners, who had been pushed into paying 56 cents per tonne of coal mined into health and welfare services. We shared views on industrial health care for about an hour. Mainly, I spoke of the lack of US research interest in pneumoconiosis and strongly advised that his powerful and wealthy Union remedy this. His retort was surprising. "Your country may have greater research investment, Dr Fletcher, but we get more coal out of the ground." Never in my years of close contact with miners' union leaders in Britain had I heard one of them boast of production.

It had been a long and fascinating tour paid for by lecture fees.[7] All along the way hospitality had been generous. I had shared views with many specialists in my field. To the two who expressed admiration of my father I sent copies of my mother's recent biography of him, *The Bright Countenance* (1957).[8] A major benefit had been in the valuable contacts made, but I was sorry that I had mainly met medical people and not gained a broader view of American society. The major concern with which I returned was of the differences between Britain and the USA in the classification of emphysema and chronic bronchitis. Already I had begun thinking of arranging an international conference to reach agreed definitions of these diseases.

Back in London I was soon reabsorbed into patient care and research. I had about twenty beds at

Charles Fletcher, consultant, Hammersmith Hospital c1959

Caroline, Susanna and Mark Fletcher, Cambridge, 1957

Lady Maisie Fletcher attending a 1950s Medical Research Council Reception

Hammersmith Hospital and plans for a second epidemiological survey to provide deeper insights into chronic bronchitis. I had become a fairly competent respiratory physician by then. In the last year I had even tried adding hypnosis to my skills to be more effective in reducing patients' anxieties. I regretted failing in this, even after instruction from my colleague Stephen Black, who was an excellent medical hypnotist, but had become more aware of the value of a strongly reassuring voice and cultivating its supportive strengths. As a result I communicated more effectively with patients and the combination of this and being tall had a significant placebo effect, which tests at Hammersmith Hospital confirmed. In them we scored patients' views of their improvement and quite a number of mine felt better even when the tests did not detect any change.

But I regretted not acquiring hypnotic skills and if I was starting in medicine again I would put them high on the list of requirements. I have always hankered after having more healing skills.

Developing helpful relationships with patients I found the most rewarding aspect of the job. I rarely indulged in private practice because I never wanted to differentiate between them on financial grounds. I was against two tier medical care and patients choosing to see me privately gained little by doing so. Always their fees went straight into a research fund. As a consultant I felt adequately remunerated by the NHS.

And I saw a wonderful and rewarding variety of patients. One of the most memorable of this period was a Thames Embankment pavement artist who had severe chronic bronchitis. This small scruffy Cockney was a revelation of brightness and confidence, claiming that his talent with chalk on pavements was unrivalled. He talked of his best pavement art works and the day during the Festival of Britain in 1951 when he had made fifteen pounds (hundreds at today's values) almost all in pennies and weighing so heavily that he took a cab home. Despite breathlessness his conversation was fascinating. I was so impressed by Mr Mannix that I took my colleague Philip Hugh-Jones to see him at work on the Embankment where most of his pictures were of British countryside scenes.

With increased competence as a respiratory physician and finding the right research niche my life had considerably brightened. And living at Richmond-on-Thames completed a very happy family picture. Lou had made a fine house on the Green into a lovely home and increasingly I enjoyed the challenge of maintaining its garden. Back in 1955 I had begun bee-keeping when a shortage of bees threatened the pollination of its fruit trees. A bee-keeping friend, Ian Wooldridge (a biochemist and later a London University professor) suggested this and provided the first hive. I have been keeping bees ever since.

Most of our neighbours on the Green at Richmond became friends and with them Lou established a society to safeguard the interests of local residents: the Richmond Society, which still flourishes. I think it was Lou's idea. John Betjeman was the main guest at its 1957 launch, which was massively attended in the Castle ballroom. Somehow, I emerged as the Society's chairman.

John Butterfield[9] (then the professor of medicine at Guy's) and his family were close Richmond neighbours. He organised splendid picnics and cricket matches on the Green, a man of colossal charm. I have already mentioned the kindness of another friend on the Green, Erasmus Barlow,[10] the psychiatrist who pointed Lou and me in the right direction at the time of my severe depression. We were particularly close to Erasmus's family and the Butterfields.

With Mark away at Eton, we were now four at dinner when I returned home each evening. But with Eton nearby we saw Mark fairly often. There was pleasure in knowing that he was doing well in science. Susanna and Caroline were attending London's Francis Holland School. What I did not appreciate was how time with my family had reduced. After dinner I usually retreated to my study and work often intruded deep into weekends, unlike in South Wales when these were largely family times. Lou was now the hub of family life. I was too immersed in professional interests. Also, Monday evenings were taken up by rehearsals of the Bach Choir, which I had joined soon after recovering from TB.[11]

In January 1958 I had an opportunity to discuss the need for internationally agreed definitions of emphysema and chronic bronchitis with close colleagues Donald Reid and John Gilson (my successor in Wales). Wisely they advised against an international conference until agreed definitions had been achieved in Britain. So my attention turned to drawing leading British experts together. We compiled an invitation list of about twenty of them and I then sought the help of the CIBA Foundation in funding and hosting a two-day meeting at its London conference centre in Portland Place. The Foundation's Director, Gordon Wolstenholme, arranged this for 28-29th September.

From February to May 1958 I presented the first series of *Your Life in Their Hands* programmes on BBC television and became the best known doctor in Britain. On average I spent about two days a week on programme preparation and could not have done this without the generous support of colleagues who stood in for me and the tolerance of my hospital chief John McMichael. He had hoped that I would undertake clinical research and I had diverted into epidemiology and television. Not enthusiastic about either field, he still managed to say in a resigned way: "We like people following their interests".

A major memory of the first *Your Life in Their Hands* (*YLITH*) series of ten programmes is of refusing to go along with plans to televise a heart operation "live". This had recently been done in America and producer Bill Duncalf and the BBC wanted impressively to do the same, but I felt that being watched by many millions would be an unreasonable burden on any surgeon engaged in complex operating. The producer and the BBC were adamant about breaking new ground and for a time I felt that I might be replaced. They had already lined up a surgeon at Birmingham to do the job. But I stuck to my recommendation that the operation be filmed instead of televised live and eventually this was accepted and the operation filmed at Birmingham. All other *YLITH* arrangements went smoothly and the series admirably demonstrated that excellence in British medicine was spread far wider than London.

But the first two programmes drew strong protests from the medical profession, which regarded their frankness as dangerous. It was emphasised that telling the public too much about medicine would lead to dramatic increases in hypochondria. Leading articles in the *British Medical Journal* condemned the series and the Postmaster General was asked to stop the BBC from continuing it. And the programme became the subject of an adjournment debate in the House of Commons (on 26 February, 1958), which the socialist MP Dr Edith Summerskill introduced to condemn our "unmasking of medicine". As the programme's presenter I received warnings from very senior members of the medical profession on how my career would be damaged by further involvement. But I knew that I was doing the right thing in reducing public ignorance about medicine, just as my father had wanted people to know more of the workings of their bodies. And the British public took to the series in millions and ensured that there would be (four) more.[12] Many at the BBC regarded *Your Life in Their Hands* as the turning point at which medicine began being talked about openly. Almost all of the early programmes were broadcast live from Alexandra Palace.

I received an honorarium of £900 for the first series and emerged with unexpected recognition as the nation's TV Doctor. I remember the initial shock of being asked what it was like to be a celebrity. All that I had done was to use my acting experience to play the kind of doctor I wished I had been and letters from admirers flooded in. After the series the BBC appointed me as its medical adviser and considered me as a possible commentator on the University Boat Race, but I was less convincing when trialled for that role in 1958. Out of touch with rowing, I lacked the facts, figures and comparisons needed to enhance the commentary. My last rowing connection had been with the Leander Club from which I resigned in 1946 when its subscription almost doubled from about five pounds to nearly ten.

My major research enterprise of 1958 was the more detailed survey of chronic bronchitis in about 400 Post Office employees (192 men and 192 women) that I had planned in 1957. This led to a much clearer definition of the disease. In addition to an extended range of questions on their coughing, phlegm production, breathlessness wheezing, duration of symptoms, impact of weather, numbers of episodes of chest illness and smoking behaviour, specimens of their sputum were collected and graded and measurements of their forced expiratory volume (FEV_1) made. This was the assessment of how much breath they could forcibly expel in one second after taking a full breath. This was done at test sessions that we arranged, using adapted laboratory spirometers. From the FEV_1 results we calculated the maximum breathing capacity (MBC) of subjects and how far it had fallen below normal levels. (Sputum samples began being collected and examined on the recommendation of my colleague Philip Hugh-Jones, who insisted that this was essential.)

The samples were collected in 30ml glass specimen bottles with metal screw caps and our survey confirmed the view that sputum production was the main defining feature of chronic bronchitis. Those with the disease characteristically produced sputum daily for over three months of the year. On the basis of sputum output patterns we divided sufferers into two groups. Those producing sputum in the morning and late in the day were categorised as Grade 1 and those producing it throughout the day as Grade 2. The results of lung function tests showed a close correlation between increasing sputum production and declining breathing capacity. Most subjects in our Grade 2 category had lost 60-80 per cent of their MBC. Also, much of the sputum that we examined was purulent, indicating a high incidence of lung infection. Lots of samples were bacterially infected.

Our findings also confirmed that smoking was a major causal factor in chronic bronchitis[13] and this led us to hypothesise that smoking caused hypersecretion of mucus by the lower bronchial tract and this increased lung susceptibility to infection, also that prolonged infection led to emphysema.

We were reaching these views by the Autumn of 1958 and during a visit to my unit by Max Wilson, a senior medical officer at the Ministry of Health, I remember stressing the importance of the Ministry advising the public of the dangers of smoking. The link between smoking and lung cancer had been known since the early 1950s and now we were showing a considerable link between smoking and chronic bronchitis and I remember my parting remark to Wilson: "When is your Health Ministry going to justify its title and tell the public of the risks?"

By this time I was convinced of the need for national anti-smoking campaigning. What I did not appreciate was the extent to which governments would avoid major anti-smoking measures for many years. Attacking a powerful industry and its highly popular products, worth many millions of pounds in tax revenue, was not an appealing commitment.

But my parting comment to Max Wilson had an unexpected outcome. About a week later I had a telephone call from George Godber,[14] the Ministry's deputy chief medical officer, suggesting that we meet and talk about what might be done to alert smokers to the risks they ran. He was concerned that his boss, the Ministry's chief medical officer, Sir John Charles, would not take the initiative. We met for lunch in October 1958, not long after the CIBA symposium that I had arranged to discuss and establish watertight definitions of chronic bronchitis and emphysema.

About twenty leading respiratory physicians, pathologists and radiologists took part in this.[15] Early discussion focused on key diagnostic characteristics and for chronic bronchitis we reached firm agreement that the coughing-up of sputum over a period of about three months in more than one year was the signature feature. Later, it was agreed that pathological evidence of the enlargement of lung air spaces become the basis of emphysema diagnosis. Then we went on to define a system of classifying forms of emphysema and grading their severity. Guy Scadding was the outstanding contributor. I took on the job of reporting the results, with the help of a small drafting committee. The final publication included belated refinements to the classification system originally drafted. Mainly our views on emphysema had needed refining.

Initially, the stages of emphysema had been classified on the basis of enlarged air spaces in the lungs and the degree of airflow obstruction. But while I was writing the CIBA conference report, Philip Hugh-Jones drew my attention to patients diagnosed with emphysema who had typical airflow obstruction, but atypical chest x-rays (lacking enlarged air spaces) and distinctly different physiological characteristics. Several other specialists confirmed these findings and we spent several months investigating this new patient category, on which we presented a paper at a conference of the Association of Physicians. The audience response was of astonishment and disbelief.

When expanded to include latest findings, the CIBA conference report on chronic bronchitis and emphysema was published in *Thorax* in 1959[16] and within the next two or three years most of its views became accepted internationally. It put the diagnosis and classification of chronic obstructive pulmonary diseases on a sound basis everywhere and was one of my most influential publications.

My most influential idea of 1958 arose during the meeting with George Godber in October. While discussing ways of alerting the public to the dangers of

139

smoking I came up with the suggestion that we ask the Royal College of Physicians to produce a report on the risks. This he liked and we subsequently discussed the idea with the president of the College, Sir Robert Platt,[17] who was immediately enthusiastic. Soon afterwards we formed, with two or three other college fellows known to have strongly anti-smoking views, a small team to draft a proposal for consideration by the College Council. The proposal: that the College set up a committee to report on the health hazards of smoking was completed in February 1959 and approved by the Council in April (with the report's remit extended to include the hazards of atmospheric pollution, although the Clean Air Act of 1956 had already begun cleaning-up the atmosphere).

I worked closely with Robert Platt in deciding who should serve on the new committee and by June 1959 its nine members had been appointed.[18] At our first meeting in July I took on the role of honorary secretary. Platt was to be an excellent chairman.

The Committee had all the expertise needed to produce a strong report. Leading chest physicians Guy Scadding and Neville Oswald took charge of reporting the medical evidence, while Jerry Morris, the head of the MRC's social medicine unit, marshalled epidemiological data. And Sir Aubrey Lewis, the president of the Royal College of Psychiatrists, contributed advice on giving-up smoking. We began meeting on a two-monthly basis.

By then I was planning a large prospective epidemiological study of chronic bronchitis. Two earlier studies had yielded valuable data, but not enough on early stages of the disease. To complete the picture we needed to study a large sample of the local workforce population over several years. With chronic bronchitis more common in men we decided to monitor a sufficiently large number of male volunteers aged between 30 and 60. The information needed would come from those who developed the disease during a study of several years. The men taking part would be randomly selected from the population of our workforce volunteers.

How many were needed was clarified by a pilot study that ran from autumn 1959 to summer 1960 and was ably arranged and managed by a new member of my Hammersmith team, research fellow Dr Cecily Tinker. The results showed that we needed to monitor about a thousand men and begin with around twelve hundred to allow for those dropping out. Again we planned to use employees of the nearby regional headquarters of the Post Office Savings Bank that had a staff of almost 2,000 and London Transport's Acton and Chiswick Engineering Workshops that employed 4,000 men.

Getting funding and securing the support of employers and trade unions were the next steps. The good links established with the Post Office led to early agreement on the involvement of savings bank employees, but negotiations with London Transport and the trade union representing its employees took considerably longer, although being the TV Doctor helped. Publications on the project have lost sight of the immense PR demands in getting it started. But arranging for the MRC to fund it went remarkably smoothly.

I went to conferences in Moscow in 1960 and 1962. On the second visit I experienced severe angina when rushing to a presentation on a bitterly cold morning. I had had a hint of angina just a few months before when rushing to attend a conference session in Bruges. I thought little of it then, but after the Moscow experience consulted a cardiology colleague in London, when it was found that the equivalent of running up three flights of stairs would trigger the pain. And I went on experiencing it often enough for it to become a burden until about a year later when it became rarer and only at times of extreme exertion.

Also on the 1962 Moscow trip (30 May – 5 June) I developed severe hypoglycaemia while queuing to see Lenin's tomb and was fortunate in being assisted by an American physician from St Louis who was attending the same conference. He strongly advised that I give up travelling overseas alone, but I did not heed his advice. I was usually good at spotting hypoglycaemia and rectifying it and at night felt safe because it woke and alerted me. Only in the late 1960s, when it did not always wake me, did I give up overseas travel alone.

At last in 1961 the lengthy prospective study of chronic bronchitis that I had been planning since 1959 got under way. The plan was to interview in summer and winter each year all contactable recruits, using the detailed respiratory questionnaire that we had developed, then assess the breathing capacity of each of them and collect sputum samples from all who were producing it. To conduct the interviews and FEV_1 tests and collect sputum samples we had recruited a team of four nurses in March 1961 and they had spent two or three months on standardising procedures. Their techniques needed to be reliably similar. Outcomes depended on this. Some of their early practice had been on inmates of Wormwood Scrubbs Prison, just a two minute walk from the Hammersmith. Among these volunteers was the notorious spy George Blake.

The prospective study took-off in July 1961 when all contactable volunteers were interviewed and data on their breathing capacity recorded during workplace visits by the nursing team. Packing the questionnaire interviewing and testing of more than a thousand men into four weeks was a colossal job for the team, but admirably completed, with large files of data resulting and many hundreds of specimen bottles of sputum for analysis. The survey requirement was for each man producing sputum to provide three samples of all that was coughed-up in the first hour of three consecutive days. We were the first investigators to collect and assess sputum samples: initially recording output volume and whether samples were "mucoid" or "infected purulent". Sputum production was a major feature of the disease.

A similar survey was scheduled for January 1962. In the intervening months the nursing team undertook much of the initial sorting and analysis of the data they had collected. This would take most of their time between winter and summer surveys.

The start of this vast project was a high point of the 1960s. The twice yearly surveys would go on until the natural history of chronic bronchitis was finally charted.

As this prospective study was taking off I completed compiling the report of the Royal College of Physicians Committee on Smoking and Health. We had ditched atmospheric pollution from our brief at the second or third of our meetings and concentrated entirely on smoking. The aim had been for a highly readable publication. We wanted it widely read. I had been asked to make it as popularly informative as my TV programmes. Usually College reports had limited circulation, but this one needed to have national impact. And about half way through its preparation the College approved recommendations for a large print-run and appointed a publicity agent to arrange a high profile launch, the first for a Royal College of Physicians report.

While finalising this report I smoked my last cigarette. I needed to match what I was recommending. I had never been a heavy smoker and gave up at the second or third attempt. I had recently celebrated my fiftieth birthday.

The 1960s had begun well. I had compiled a high-profile report on Smoking and Health,[19] launched the largest research project of my career, completed a second successful television series of *Your Life in Their Hands* (in 1961),[20] received an NHS merit award that almost doubled my salary, and broadcasting had not damaged my career. I had become a Council member of the Royal College of Physicians[21] and a World Health Organisation consultant.[22]

Chapter 8
Tracking the natural history of chronic bronchitis, promotion to a university reader's post, initiating postgraduate GP education on TV

1962 began with the second survey of men taking part in the prospective study, who had first been investigated in July 1961. We would go on surveying about a thousand of them, twice yearly, for as long as it took to describe the complete natural history of chronic bronchitis. There was still a lot to discover.

January and July were the months of our winter and summer surveys and after each of them the main occupation of my small research team was the sorting and analysing of the data collected. The nurses who had interviewed the men and assessed their breathing spent several weeks laboriously involved in sorting many thousands of questionnaire findings and punching them onto punch cards, together with FEV_1 details and sputum analysis results. The results for each man investigated were logged onto one punch card, then all the cards were sorted into results categories by running them through a mechanical sorting machine. Further analysis of results was then undertaken with a noisy, electrically powered calculating machine. The age of computers was still dawning.

Supervising the data processing was the statistician David Hill (the son of medical statistician and trials expert Sir Austin Bradford Hill) who had been involved since the project-planning stage. The processing of data after each survey took three or four months, after which the team of nurses began preparing for the next survey.

Being together in modest accommodation assisted close and friendly team relationships. The hut that we occupied was not much longer than a cricket pitch, about 20 feet wide and partitioned into three sections: a small

145

entrance area, a main work area and finally my office, dominated by the large roll-top desk that I used and an enormous leather armchair for visitors. Along one wall of the work area and through into my office stretched a laboratory bench, with sinks and gas and electric points, often with stacked boxes of sputum specimen bottles awaiting examination. The rest of this laboratory-cum-general work area had several tables at which team members sat when sorting and processing data. Stacks of files adorned most of them. The secretary of the unit, the very resourceful Rosemary Lee, occupied the small entrance area. The primitive sorting machine was in a nearby hut. Apart from the main block, the Hammersmith was largely a hutted hospital. Our hut was between two wings of the main building.[1]

1962 was an outstanding year. *Smoking and Health*, the RCP Report that I had compiled lifted anti-smoking campaigning to a new level. Launched at a press conference at the RCP on 8th March it had considerable media and newspaper publicity resulting in all ten thousand copies being sold in a week and a second print-run urgently arranged. Until then anti-smoking publicity had teetered ineffectively. The publicity agent appointed by the RCP had done an excellent promotional job. This was the first time that a College report had such a prominent launch. Over the next eighteen months over eighty thousand copies were sold, more than five thousand in the USA. The impact of the Report in America led to President J F Kennedy's request for the US Surgeon General to begin producing annual reports on smoking and health.[2]

Soon after the launch of *Smoking and Health* I made a memorable visit to the Isle of Wight to bid for two small cottages at Newtown that were being auctioned as one lot on 16th March. We had long admired the location of the short terrace of former coastguard cottages of which they were a part, and Lou's sister Emy had told us of their sale and expected price of £700-£800. I decided to go as high as £1500 to get them and felt fortunate when bidding stopped at my last-chance bid of £1550. That was a wonderful moment (on 16 March). We had the holiday property of our dreams: two cottages for converting into one, with glorious outlook over salt marsh to the Solent. We all loved the Island. To Lou it was going home. Now, instead of renting holiday cottages each year we had our own. A better investment of my recent TV fees would have been difficult to find.

Not long after this Isle of Wight visit I had the news that I had been appointed as a London University Reader in Clinical Epidemiology and further recognition followed at the Royal Society of Medicine where I became president of the epidemiology section. Also, following the success of *Smoking and Health*, I had an invitation from Penguin Books to be the lead author of a Penguin Classic to spread greater awareness of the risks, economics and sociology of smoking, and provide guidelines on giving up.[3]

This project was under discussion when I went to Moscow in the late spring of 1962 (31 May-3 June) to attend a conference on diseases of the respiratory tract, from which I returned via Copenhagen for a World Health Organisation meeting of chest specialists (on 4 June). I was strongly committed to international collaboration in my specialty and while in Moscow accepted invitations to return at the end of the year to attend a national conference on chest diseases and discuss research developments with Ministry of Health officials.

Not long after the first visit to Moscow I flew to Chicago to give a paper at the Annual Conference of the American Association of Chest Physicians (on 23 June, 1962). The trip had been planned to include visits to major hospital departments of chest medicine and centres of research interest in Chicago, then Boston. The main objective was to spread the British view of chronic bronchitis as a disease of considerable importance. American doctors still tended to regard it too lightly. One specialist that I met on this trip dismissed it as "a nuisance more than a serious disorder". I spoke of the extent to which it was disabling and potentially lethal and of the three developmental categories into which we in Britain were classifying it.

On my visits to Chicago hospitals I saw several clear-cut cases of chronic bronchitis that had been diagnosed as emphysema.

Before the conference I spent an interesting day at the vast Western Electricity Plant on an outer edge of the City where a major survey of employees' chest diseases was under way and using a version of the questionnaire developed by my team at the Hammersmith.[4] I advised that investigations of sputum be added to the survey.

At the Hammersmith we had recently begun investigating the eosinophil content of survey sputum samples. These white blood cells (of the immune system) were known to collect at infection sites and we were interested in what might be deduced from their concentrations.

The last few days of this trip were in Boston where I spent time with Dr Ben Ferris who was conducting studies of respiratory problems in long-serving tunnel maintenance workers who had been exposed to automobile exhaust fumes for more than a decade.[5] Later, I spent time at Boston's Mallory Institute of Pathology where impressive studies of bacterial colonisation of the bronchial tree were going on.[6] On the final day of the visit I had a tour of an impressive private lung disease institute with its founder (Dr Richard Overholt). While there I met the lawyer (James E McLaughlin) representing the family of one of the Institute's cancer patients in legal action against the manufacturer of the cigarettes[7] that he had smoked for more than thirty years. Until then I had not appreciated the extent to which such ground-breaking cases were a complicated struggle against skilled tobacco company defences, as well as legal and political attitudes. The case had already had two unsuccessful Federal appellate court trials, but was due to be heard before the US Court of Appeal in Pennsylvania in October. I was asked of expert witnesses from England that I could recommend. Being invited to serve in this capacity was a surprise on my return home.

I returned (on 5 July) just as my team's 1962 summer survey of men taking part in the prospective study of chronic bronchitis was under way. Again the team of four nurses packed into four weeks all the long questionnaire interviews and FEV1 assessments required to update our information on more than a thousand subjects. Again, men producing sputum were asked to collect the output of the first hour of three consecutive days and post these samples in envelopes provided to my Unit for investigation.[8]

During the follow-up months of data processing I arranged updating meetings with the employers and trade union representatives of the men taking part. At the one with Post Office Savings Bank managers and union officials in October I arrived just as news of the Cuban Missile Crisis had broken and had the challenge of easing tensions among a group feeling that another day might not arrive.

A few days later my son went up to Cambridge, to my college as a medical student, the fourth Fletcher to make this step. I could not have felt more elated.

Shortly afterwards I flew to Pittsburgh for three days (7-9 October) to give evidence as an expert witness in the US Appeal Court in the case against the makers of Chesterfield Cigarettes that I had heard about on my last visit to the USA. As in two earlier trials, powerful tobacco company lawyers were wonderfully adept at defusing claims, principally by casting doubt on the statistics of tobacco health risks and claiming that the manufacturer could not have been aware of any of the dangers when the plaintiff became a smoker of the brand, also that the plaintiff had gone on smoking the product long after some of the dangers had become clear and so was guilty of contributory negligence. I was astounded that a company that had blatantly advertised the safety of its cigarettes in such terms as *Nose, Throat and Accessory Organs Not Adversely Affected by Chesterfields* was not judged as culpable. Over the next few years I became increasingly aware of the skilled defence tactics of this highly dangerous industry and involved increasingly in campaigning against its products.

Before the year ended, Greater London experienced another major fog that lasted from 4th-7th of December. Sulphur dioxide levels went up, but those of other atmospheric pollutants remained far lower than in the Great London Smog of 1952. There were still enough casualties to put London hospitals under heavy pressure, but far fewer deaths than in 1952 (sixty in contrast to several thousands). Air clean-up measures were working. In my ward at the Hammersmith I set up Airwick-type bottles containing ammonia, one on each bedside locker, with hopes of neutralising some of the atmospheric sulphur dioxide. But the effectiveness of this shot-in-the-dark initiative we never had time to assess.

My team went into the January 1963 survey of men taking part in our prospective study of chronic bronchitis particularly interested in what effect this recent and dense four-day fog would have had on the FEV1 results of those with airflow obstruction. But no discernable impact was found.

The data from each survey took us a step nearer to a complete picture of the natural history of chronic bronchitis. At various points along this journey we included additional lines of investigation. On one occasion measurements of airways resistance in 752 of our volunteers were made before and after they had smoked a cigarette to check on whether increases in resistance resulted. The answer was no and ended speculation on the immediate effects of smoking. The testing was done in a whole body plethysmograph, a sealed cabinet in which breathing could be finely appraised, and carried out by Dr (later professor) John Alpers, an Australian on attachment to the Unit. For this work we used a borrowed plethysmograph and took it to the men's workplaces in a caravan that we bought and fitted-out. During two other surveys electrocardiograms and blood pressure measurements were recorded to assist research being carried out by Dr (later professor) Geoffrey Rose of the London School of Hygiene and Tropical Medicine.

Following the January 1963 survey I spent a month in India (from 16 February to 16 March) on a lecture trip organised by the British Council. Lou accompanied me and we travelled widely, enjoying the rich cultural diversity and splendours of a land of which we knew little. I lectured at a number of medical colleges and talked on chest diseases with specialists at several main hospitals. British Council arrangements were excellent in providing an even balance of commitments and sightseeing leisure. Occasionally, I did too much and paid the price by becoming hypoglycaemic.

In England such episodes were far more occasional, but all the members of my team had become good at spotting the signs and swiftly remedying my glucose deficiency, particularly the nurses. By the time that I returned from India they had abstracted most of the data from the January 1963 survey questionnaires: about a thousand of them, each with several dozen responses.

In addition to clinical and research commitments I was still heavily involved in television broadcasting and in 1963 presented a fourth series of *Your Life in Their Hands*. Following the first series in 1959 there had been a two year gap, during which the video-recording of TV programmes began, then from 1961 a series of eight video-recorded programmes each year. *YLITH* had retained high viewing figures and overcome early professional objections to its unmasking of medicine. After the first series I had become the BBC's medical adviser and a while later involved in short presentations, broadcast weekly under the title of *Television Doctor*, fifteen-minute early evening slots on topical medical interests. A supportive Hammersmith Hospital gave me the day needed each fortnight to record the next two programmes. Wherever I went I seemed to meet people who had watched a recent programme and had questions to ask. Many commented on how I translated medical complexities into understandable terms. Over the years of talking with

151

patients I had concentrated on this. I owed a background in plain speaking to my mother. I had developed her habit of speaking aloud while having a bath and reducing views and comment to simplest terms. Consequently, I used words of few syllables when talking with patients and broadcasting.

Around this time my mother had a health scare. She rang and said that she had suddenly been unable to use her right hand and had problems with talking. After discussing how serious this might be with a neurology colleague, Christopher Pallis, I cancelled appointments and went to Westmorland to be with her. She was eighty-two and had been living there for more than a decade at her family home, Ellergreen.[9] Until now she had been robustly healthy and a great walker. I spent a week with her and then returned, relieved that her speech and hand movements were improving. Progress reports went on being increasingly good and she made a complete recovery within a month or two.

In the summer of 1963 our daughter, Susanna, moved a step closer to a career as an art teacher, with a place at the Froebel Institute, Roehampton, for teacher training. Mark at Cambridge had transferred from medicine to reading Law. Caroline, our younger daughter, was still at the Francis Holland School. By now Mark and Susanna wished that we lived nearer to central London and its range of attractions for young adults. Even Caroline was soon sharing the view that they were missing-out and we should relocate.

An impressive development in my specialist field was the measurement of "peak flow", pioneered by my dearest friend and former PRU colleague Martin Wright. His remarkable inventiveness in the mid-1950s (1956) produced the peak flow meter, an ingenious simple and portable device that measures a person's maximum speed of expiration. I was among the first to emphasise its massive clinical and research potential and over the next decade and a half it slowly gained acceptance as the best way of assessing airflow through the bronchi and the degree of airways obstruction. At Hammersmith Hospital we had been using the peak flow meter since the early 1960s to discover how far individuals differed in performance according to comparisons with sets of normal values that Wright had drawn up: the Wright Scales of Normal Peak Expiratory Flow (PEF) for men and women of different ages and heights. There would have been advantages in using PEF measurements and the Wright Index in our prospective study of chronic bronchitis, but the benefits had not been fully appreciated in 1959-1960 when the study was being designed and we had committed to FEV_1 measurements. It took the medical profession almost twenty years to fully grasp the advantages of using Wright's peak flow meter, but it is now used everywhere and the simple, cheap and highly portable plastic version of the instrument that he produced in the mid-1970s used by millions, particularly asthma sufferers to monitor their bronchial resistance. And the breathalyser ("alcometer") that Martin developed is still in wide use by UK traffic police for roadside checks on drivers.

My team's amassing of data on chronic bronchitis reached its fourth year in 1964 and looked likely to continue for another four. Again our nurses undertook the intensive January and July workplace surveys of the volunteers taking part in the study. Almost a thousand were still under surveillance. Losses were less than ten per cent per year from the fairly stable workforces involved.

About fifteen per cent of my professional commitment went into this long-running project, another ten per cent into TV broadcasting and committee service, but mainly I was involved in patient care. My clinical team at Hammersmith Hospital had twenty inpatient beds and four outpatient clinics each week. Assisting patients was the prime source of satisfaction.

A growing concern of the 1960s was the plight of those who were terminally and horrendously ill, with nothing left to live for and who asked to be put out of their misery. I could not have been in greater sympathy with the pleas of several who asked for my help. I judged their requests as entirely reasonable, but there was little that clinicians could do to assist them. Euthanasia was a criminal offence and against set-in-stone professional codes and moral attitudes. Increasingly, I longed for reasonable debate on the right of patients in desperately hopeless situations to have medical help in dying. Changing political, professional and public attitudes in favour of this looked a mountain to climb, and I appreciated how difficult it would be to legalise euthanasia for a deserving few without opening chances of misuse, but I was convinced that change was needed.

To me there seemed little difference between assisting the deaths of patients wishing to end intolerable terminal suffering and the selectiveness we applied to resuscitation. At the Hammersmith and in many hospitals at that time there were regular meetings of senior clinical staff to decide on who should and who should not be resuscitated. I felt that this was euthanasia that had slipped in under the radar. Each time a patient justifiably implored my help in dying I deplored the inconsistency in medical attitudes that held me back.

One of the first pleas to dramatically register was from the widow of a former Hammersmith colleague who had a severe stroke at his funeral and came onto John McMichael's ward massively paralysed. As a friend I visited her there and had her sad request for help. "I have nothing left to live for, Charles, and I am not going to survive this stroke, so please help me to go," she implored me. I felt that she was being eminently sensible, but was in a hopeless position. She was McMichael's patient and he would have been horrified by any reference to assisted death. Consequently, she lingered-on for another three months and died in deepest misery. Her plight made a deep impression on me. That was in the late-1950s.

Then, three or four years later, I had a similar plea from one of my patients, a man with very severe airways obstruction who in deepest despair gulped a wish not to endure struggling for breath any longer. "I don't want another night of it" he said. And I asked him "Do you

154

really want to go to sleep?" His response could not have been more positive. A while later, I double checked on this and on receiving the same reply gave him heavy sedation. He died that night and for the first time I crossed the line into criminal practice, but believed that I had made the right decision in ending a life that had deteriorated too painfully beyond hope.

Being as sure as possible of a patient's wish for assistance is crucial. This could not have been better demonstrated just a few months later when a patient with similar severe breathing difficulties implored my help. Asked whether he really did want to drift off into sleep, he replied "Only if I was sure to wake up, doctor". He was not wishing death.

Lou and I took a short break in the USA in September 1964, as soon as initial sorting of the July survey data on our prospective study volunteers was completed. In addition to holiday travels in America I met and advanced collaborative links with several clinicians and researchers visited before. I was pleased to discover that the questionnaire on respiratory disease experience developed by my team at Hammersmith Hospital was assisting several US projects. By now, its use had spread to a number of countries.

A main event of 1965 was settling into a new family home in Chelsea at Drayton Gardens SW10. I would have preferred to remain in Richmond, but Lou and our children made a strong case for the change.

We arrived in Chelsea soon after my final series of *Your Life in Their Hands* ended. After five series (1959, 61, 62, 63 and 64) the BBC had decided to give *YLITH* a break. But I continued my weekly *Television Doctor* broadcasts and as the BBC's medical adviser, a role that I had taken on after the first *YLITH* series and which provided similar remuneration.[10] A major condition of my BBC contract was that I would not appear on ITV, with which there was astounding rivalry in these early years of independent television.

Not long before the final series of *Your Life in Their Hands* in 1964, I began attending meetings of the London Medical Group, a forum set up a year earlier for the discussion of medical ethics,[11] and forerunner of the Society for the Study of Medical Ethics, of which I was on the planning committee in 1965. I hoped for increasing debate on euthanasia. At one of the early meetings of the London Medical Group I remember Dr Cicely Saunders, the pioneer of the British hospice movement, emphasising that there are always ways in which terminally ill patients can be made comfortable and kept from suffering, without hastening their end. She was talking mainly of patients in late stages of cancer, where that is true, but my concern was for those beyond palliative help, such as severe stroke victims left with right-sided hemiplegia, who can neither talk nor use the right side of their bodies. I believed that those wishing release from such incapacity should have the right to medical assistance.

By the end of 1965 I had acclimatised to living in Chelsea. Giving up the fine garden developed at Richmond-on-Thames had been a wrench, but developing the garden of our Isle of Wight holiday cottage compensated. In the three years since we bought it we had renovated and made extensive alterations to the building and I had tamed the wilderness that had been the garden and done much planting. Family breaks there were loved.

Mark spent the latter part of the year in the USA after completing his Cambridge Law degree. Back in London, his training to be a solicitor would stretch through 1966, a year in which Susanna completed teacher training and joined the staff of a Pimlico school and Caroline became Head Girl of the Francis Holland School.

Early in 1966 I went on a two month lecture and leisure trip to Australia, New Zealand, Hong Kong and Japan, which took most of March and April and ended at a conference in Athens. Over the last three years I had spent more time on improvements to our Isle of Wight holiday home and garden than on overseas travels, but an accumulation of invitations to lecture and visit hospitals led eventually to this lengthy tour. Lou accompanied me and shared many sight-seeing opportunities. While we travelled, my team at the Hammersmith processed the data collected in our tenth survey of men taking part in the long-term prospective study of chronic bronchitis. Since 1961 vast masses of data and been processed and the end was still not quite in sight. Latest news of our findings I shared with respiratory specialists during this 1966 tour and had the benefit of contact with other research developments.

This was also the year in which my main contribution as the BBC's adviser on medical programmes began to change. With the postgraduate education of GPs lagging in development and many practitioners lacking up-to-date knowledge I had come to the conclusion that instructive TV programmes would be an excellent way of updating them. Back in 1965 I had shared my views with leaders of the Association for the Study of Medical Education,[12] who had established a committee to consider the possibilities. Feeling strongly supported, I eventually talked with Robert Reid, the BBC TV producer most suited to such a challenge, and managed to overcome his initial resistance to the idea of medical education programmes for GPs. That was in 1966 and preparations for a first series of monthly programmes to be piloted in the London Region were to take eighteen months. They were to be broadcast late at night after normal programme transmission had ended. They were not the first TV programmes aimed at updating GPs. There had been a precedent in Scotland where Scottish Television had successfully presented two or three late-night up-dating programmes for the region's practitioners. I was pleased that the BBC had now taken on the challenge and that I was involved in the planning.

My second international trip of 1966 was to Aspen, Colorado, in June, to an international conference on emphysema. With the complexities of diseases of chronic airflow obstruction still being clarified these were occasions for valuable updating. There was a lot of clarification going on.

In England I had recently become a member of the Central Health Services Council (CHSC) and its Standing Medical Advisory Committee. The CHSC was the main advisory body serving the NHS and I valued involvement in its deliberations, especially on improvements to hospital care. A year later, in 1967, I accepted an invitation to serve on the Health Education Council (HEC), the new body intended to lead health education nationally from 1968.[13] Becoming its vice-chairman strengthened my interests in health promotion, but getting this new central health education agency established proved a slow process. A worse start would have been difficult to achieve. Ian Sutherland's *Health Education, Half a Policy*[14] provides a detailed account of the troubled beginnings of this QUANGO: ranging from inadequate funding and political vulnerability to discord between chairman and director general.[15] But throughout all this I went on contributing to direction-finding debate hoping for an influential organisation to evolve.

A lot of time and thought in 1967 went into planning the first BBC TV series of GP-updating programmes, which were to begin in 1968 under the title *Medicine Today*. They were to go out monthly and be trialled in the London region. On the recommendation of John Butterfield, my former neighbour, the organising committee appointed John Stuart Cameron,[16] a Guy's registrar with a strong amateur dramatics background, to help plan and present them.

The high spot of 1967 was the marriage of my daughter Susanna to the wonderfully ambitious and talented young lawyer, Nicholas Lyell,[17] a barrister of the Inner Temple with farsighted political aspirations. By then Mark had qualified as a solicitor and was in articled clerkship at the London firm of Coward Chance. Caroline had begun a fascinating series of between school and university jobs. At the family holiday cottage I spent numerous weekends establishing an orchard on an adjacent piece of leased land and setting-up bee hives.

In September 1967 I attended the first World Conference on Smoking and Health at New York. En route, I stopped off in Montreal and London Ontario to strengthen collaborative links with departments of respiratory medicine and colleagues there, and provide updates on my prospective study of chronic bronchitis.

Recently, I had been appointed to the Council of the International Epidemiological Association (IEA), after membership of this emerging organisation for nearly a decade. It had originated back in 1954 as a fairly informal "international corresponding club" to promote communication between physicians working in social and preventive medicine departments. And it had grown impressively, with a first international meeting at the CIBA Foundation in London in 1956 at which members from about 20 (18) countries took part. Soon afterwards a Study Group on Current Epidemiological Research was established and a major international conference convened. At a second conference in 1959 the organisation's current title was acquired. I became a member at about that time and attended the third international meeting on the island of Korčula, Yugoslavia, in 1961. By then, the fast growing association had the backing of the World Health Organisation. This 1961 IEA conference had fitted into a family holiday break across Europe by car.

My first IEA Council meeting was in the USA in April 1968 when the programme of the next international meeting (at Primosten, Yugoslavia, in August) was drawn up. This four week trip, with Lou, included visits to Chicago, Dallas, Tucson, Boston, New Haven and Jamaica, and opportunities to liaise with specialist colleagues. Four months later, liaising with international colleagues continued at the IEA Primosten conference. Advancing recognition of the character and importance of chronic bronchitis was always my main objective. There was still a lot of confusion.

My son Mark married in November 1968 and there were family celebrations. Soon afterwards I had the surprise of being awarded the Bissett Hawkins Gold Medal of the Royal College of Physicians in recognition of my research and contributions to public knowledge of medicine. The early TV broadcasting on medical matters for which I had been sternly criticised by many in the profession a decade before now had an accolade.

And my latest TV initiative, *Medicine Today*, the late-night programme designed to update GPs, had begun well. A pilot series of ten programmes had been broadcast in the London region and watched by 1 in 3 GPs. On the basis of their feedback, plans to broadcast another series nationwide were going ahead. Initially, the programme had attracted strong criticism from many in the profession about possible damage to GP-patient relationships: if patients watched the programme and GPs did not and were found inadequately informed. My emphatic view was that GPs should be making every effort to keep up to date and this programme was a way of doing so at a time when GPs lacked adequate postgraduate instruction.

This initiative in postgraduate GP education was to continue for eight years[18] (a total of 80 programmes) and I went on chairing the programme planning committee. Audience research continued showing that about 30 per cent of GPs tuned-in monthly, also that the programmes attracted a lay audience of at least half a million, a significant bonus in public knowledge of medicine.

1969 was the year in which my long-running prospective study ended. Over the eight years in which it had been running there had been enough new cases of chronic bronchitis within our volunteer population for us to begin assembling a definitive picture of its early stages from the data collected. Data analysis was in the capable hands of Richard Peto[19] of the MRC Statistical Research Unit, who had been recommended for the job by Richard Doll when David Hill moved on in 1967 after we had begun considering a replacement. His competence as a statistician had never been matched by interest in the project.

Peto had a difficult task ahead. The project could have been better designed for statistical analysis, but over the next four years, within a work schedule of massive competing commitments, he extracted all that could be deduced from the data amassed.

I regret never being competent at statistics. It has been a considerable weakness of my epidemiological career. Even when I work out a standard deviation, which is a basic requirement, I struggle due to extremely poor mathematics. Always, I have relied on competent colleagues.

Richard Peto's analysis of the prospective study data was to have major revelations, including the surprise finding that not all smokers are at risk of chronic bronchitis, also statistical contradiction of our original view that mucus hypersecretion and bronchial infection cause chronic airflow obstruction to progress more rapidly and that prolonged infection led to emphysema. But with the analysis not completed until 1974, detailed results were not published until 1976, and will be summarised when we reach that point in the story. They justified the considerable commitment of my small team at the Hammersmith, which my colleague Cecily Tinker splendidly managed on a day-to-day basis. All members of the team deserve mention[20] and tribute is also due to the 792 of the original 1136 men who took part in the study from beginning to end.

With the prospective study concluded my research attention turned to the assessment of the new lower-nicotine, lower-tar "safer" cigarettes that the tobacco industry had begun marketing to combat increasing national awareness of the dangers of smoking. A lot of money was being invested in the production of tobacco substitutes that could be blended into cigarettes to reduce tobacco content. ICI had become involved in producing a "safer" smoking material. My interest was in how far cigarettes branded as "safer" reduced the risks of chronic bronchitis developing. They needed testing and by 1969 I had begun contemplating the kind of trial needed.

For respiratory medicine the huge advance of 1969 was the introduction of the bronchodilator salbutamol, the first inhaled asthma drug. Just a small dose relieved asthmatic airways obstruction almost instantaneously. Before, we had much slower acting muscle relaxants like ephedrine hydrochloride and the problems of their side effects. The designer-drug salbutamol was the creation of David Jack[21] and his team at the Glaxo subsidiary, Allen and Hanbury, who would advance asthma treatment further in the 1970s by the production of beclomethasone (the first inhaled steroid to suppress the inflammation of asthma). Over the next few years I was to become increasingly interested in the better education of asthma sufferers to ensure that they had self-care instruction to match the quality of the medication available. Later this led to a patient education association of which there will be more to say. On my Hammersmith ward I had seen too many grim asthma attacks not to be deeply committed to reducing their incidence.

I emerged from the 1960s a strong campaigner against smoking. For a respiratory physician there could not have been a better cause. And with the long-running study of chronic bronchitis just completed I seemed on the threshold of writing a definitive text on the disease. I had spent about a twentieth of the decade on overseas travels advancing discussion of chronic obstructive lung diseases and supporting the early development of epidemiological networks. In addition, I had helped to establish a forum[22] in which such long-taboo subjects as euthanasia were being formally discussed. I hoped that debate would lead eventually to clear and justifiable views of when assisted death should be a medical option. They were long overdue for a caring profession.

My crusading zeal advanced considerably in the Sixties.

London Transport's Acton Engineering Works

163

London Transport's Chiswick Engineering Works

164

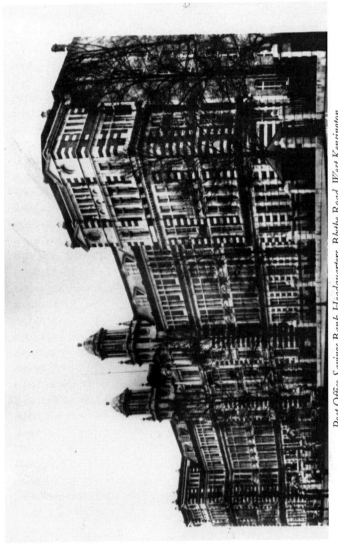

Post Office Savings Bank Headquarters, Blythe Road, West Kensington

Chapter 9
The founding of ASH,
becoming a professor at sixty,
two major publications,
retirement from the NHS in 1976

The 1970s began with anti-smoking assignments. Eight years after the Royal College of Physicians published its first *Smoking and Health* report the need for a second was recognised. Following the temporary impact of the first, too little had been done to achieve a decline in smoking in Britain. Governments had dragged their feet in combating the problem, reluctant to antagonise a powerful and popular industry of high value to the Exchequer. And many MPs had lucrative tobacco company links. Apart from the 1964 ban on the television advertising of cigarettes, there had been little political progress.

My main commitment of 1970 was compiling the second anti-smoking report of the Royal College of Physicians. As for the first report, I worked with a small team of expert colleagues in drafting this and then drew up the final document, with as powerful an introduction as I could produce. The College president, Sir Max Rosenheim, provided exemplary support throughout.

While compiling the report I discussed with him my view that a pressure organisation was needed to permanently campaign against smoking and the tobacco industry. But I was not the first to recommend this. I discovered that RCP colleagues Sir Francis Avery Jones and Keith Ball had already done so. And based on our recommendations Rosenheim drew the RCP into establishing an independent anti-smoking body, the Council for Action on Smoking and Health, soon known by the acronym ASH, which began operating in 1971, with a £125,000 start-up grant from the Secretary of State for Social Services Sir Keith Joseph.[1] The Council for Action on Smoking and Health drew together representatives of various health care professions and as its chairman I worked closely with honorary secretary Keith Ball[2] in establishing an operational base: a London office and small initial action team. Tracking smoking-related research and disseminating anti-smoking information were initial commitments. Beyond belief was how influential the organisation would become. Max Rosenheim has never been adequately credited with creating it.

The second anti-smoking assignment of 1970 was preparing a report for the 23rd World Health Assembly at Geneva in May 1971, stressing the extent of smoking risks and importance of anti-smoking measures spreading internationally. I was invited by the director general of WHO to co-author this with the leading US anti-smoking campaigner, Daniel Horn,[3] a statistician who had done much in the last two decades to define the cancer risks associated with smoking. We collaborated well in this challenging task and used the opportunity to stress to an international assembly the importance of curbing tobacco product advertising.

Other satisfaction in 1970 came from assisting the operational development of the recently formed Health Education Council (HEC). Formed in 1967 it had struggled into existence, but I valued opportunities of advising on its early campaigning and education initiatives, once it was up and running. Its earliest anti-smoking initiative had been a poster campaign late in 1969 stressing: *Why Learn About Smoking the Hard Way?* Serving as vice-chairman of the HEC, and as an interim chairman in 1968 (following the resignation of the Council's first chairman[4]) vastly advanced my understanding of the difficult challenges and politics of health education.

Fitted into September 1970 was an international conference on smoking and health at Tucson, Arizona, then intelligence-sharing visits to departments of respiratory medicine in Boston and Canada.[5] Before the year ended I had begun planning with Stanley Freedman, the latest registrar in my Hammersmith Department, a study of the advantages to smokers that there might be in smoking the reduced-nicotine, reduced-tar cigarettes being promoted as "safer" by the manufacturers. Their tobacco content had been reduced by 30%, using the tobacco substitute NSM (New Smoking Material).

1971 began memorably, with the publication of the second RCP report: *Smoking and Health Now* and the inaugural meeting of ASH in January, followed by an International Epidemiological Association meeting in Warsaw in April, then the presentation at the World Health Assembly in Geneva in May of the WHO report that I had prepared with Daniel Horn. Banning smoking at meetings of the Assembly was a first outcome of this report. And *Smoking and Health Now* had well-publicised impact on smoking in Britain. Levels dropped for a month or two and within the professional classes there were permanent reductions. In addition, the report had influence at the DHSS, where the Secretary of State for Social Services Keith Joseph accepted the recommendation that cigarette packs should carry a health warning, also our recommendation that lists of the tar and nicotine content of different brands should be published.

I became sixty in June. My mother had reached 90. We enjoyed visiting her in Westmorland and remaining in close contact. Recently she had moved from an apartment in her former family home, Ellergreen, to share a small nearby house with younger sister, Margaret Cropper,[6] a remarkably lovely woman and aunt with a wonderful gift of telling Westmorland stories and writing poetry. The *Westmorland Gazette* published many of her works, including her long story of Mary Crosby set in verse. The poem overleaf typifies her caring sensitivity and moves me deeply.

This she wrote in later years, possibly based on personal experience. *Winter Peace*[6] is more typical of her poetry.

I fitted several international visits into the second half of 1971, to attend meetings and conferences or discuss research advances with respiratory specialists. The first

I'll Hold Your Hand

They were unkind steps,
No rail for the old and shaken.
And there they lay.
Most days on my way home
They brought me to a stand,
A halting moment.
If you should fall, they said,
If you should fall....

I was standing there feeling rather fearful and old
When I heard a voice behind me,
A childish voice, almost too soft to be heard,
And into my hand a very small hand came,
Peacefully holding mine.
It was such a small hand,
A six year old's, perhaps,
Holding my withered fingers in innocent grasp.

It was matched by the sweetest voice
And the confident message:
I'll hold your hand 'til you get down those steps.
I don't think I could have fallen after that.
It would have been blasphemy to think of falling.
So, step-by-step, I went hopefully to the road.
Then I dared to look round,
But the child had vanished.

I never saw her, but something stirred in me.
Someone had come. Someone had helped me.

(Originally published in the Westmorland Gazette)

was to Yugoslavia and Germany for conferences. The second was to Canada and Boston to advance the links with specialists there.

1972 brought an unexpected invitation from the Nuffield Provincial Hospitals Trust (NPHT) for me to be its next Rock Carling fellow.[7] Based on my experience as a television presenter and in health education, the Trust wanted me to prepare a monograph on communicating with the public on medical matters. I was flattered to be asked. Richard Doll and Archie Cochrane had been recent Rock Carling fellows. Archie's Rock Carling monograph, *Effectiveness and Efficiency, random reflections on health services*[8] was about to be published and send a clarion call for evidence-based and cost-effective health care. No-one, not even Archie, anticipated its profound impact.

Before beginning the Rock Carling fellowship assignment I completed arrangements for my Unit's investigation of the effects of reduced-nicotine, reduced-tar cigarettes, which were being marketed as "safer" on the basis of having a 70-30 per cent blend of tobacco and New Smoking Material made from cellulose. Because of the difficulties of persuading many smokers to give up, it was important to test the benefits there might be in taking-up less harmful cigarettes. In this investigation we were backed by funding from the tobacco industry. My latest registrar at the Hammersmith, Stanley Freedman, took the lead in planning it, assisted in its statistical design by Michael Healy of the Northwick Park Clinical Research Centre.

Seeking smoker volunteers to take part began in May 1972. The plan was to recruit male smokers in the 25-57 age range into a randomly controlled crossover trial lasting 20 months.[9] Men selected would be matched into pairs on the basis of age, cigarette consumption, FEV1 score and similar coughing and sputum production. For nine months one of each pair would be provided with NSM-containing cigarettes and the other with 100% tobacco cigarettes. They would be closely monitored on a monthly basis with FEV1 and vital lung capacity measured and estimates of coughing and sputum made, based on a set of grades. After nine months the smoking arrangements would be reversed, with men who had been smoking 100% tobacco cigarettes switched to ones with NSM, and their counterparts switched to smoking ones with 100% tobacco.

After checking that all volunteers were heavily committed smokers who were prepared to smoke only the cigarettes that we supplied without charge, two hundred of them were selected and the study begun in August 1972. From that point they were visited monthly by members of the small nursing team trained to collect the data required and supply cigarettes for the next month. Stanley Freedman took charge of operations.

My daughter Caroline's going up to Cambridge in October was well celebrated. Aged 23 there had been quite a gap between school and university, but some useful work skills acquired en route. Interests in religion drew her into reading theology.

Not until late in 1972 did I begin grappling with the Rock Carling fellowship assignment. Over the next six months I needed to produce a monograph of more than 30,000 words on communicating with the public about medicine. This I might have managed without too much trouble, but I began thinking more widely about communication within medicine: between doctors and between doctors and patients. This led me into unknown territory and unsure of how to progress. Eventually I talked about literature searches with the librarian at Hammersmith Hospital, who mentioned that a recently retired librarian of the National Institute of Medical Research (Rudolph Klein) might undertake them. This he did and produced a considerable list of references. In addition to working through these publications I gathered the views of a range of colleagues on communication in their fields. This intelligence gathering stretched across the early months of 1973.

During this period I learned that my appointment at the Postgraduate Medical School at the Hammersmith was to become professorial in October. The step from reader to professor in clinical epidemiology had been a long time coming and there was relief that it had, just three years from retirement.

Among the worst moments of my life was the death of my mother in March. News that she had suffered a severe stroke caught up with Lou and me during a brief visit to Cambridge when Caroline was in the university crew preparing for the Women's University Boat Race. I had just had the thrill of seeing the crew in action on the river when the call came through. Hastily joined by my sister Anne, Lou and I then drove to Westmorland.

Mother was aware of who we were and able to feebly communicate, but very disturbed and not totally coherent. It was then that I remembered a conversation we had had about death at the time of a previous health scare and my agreement to help her over any difficulties she might have in dying. Then when the nurse who spent much of the night with her reported that she had been anxiously calling for me I realised that she was hoping for that help. So I said to the GP when he arrived that I would like to have something to help her sleep and avoid the distress she had suffered that night. He offered to send along some Valium, but I suggested that Omnipon[10] might be better and this he sent.

I then had the terrible job of giving it to her, which was shockingly difficult, but I knew that it was the right thing to do and gave her a large injection, after which she did not regain consciousness. I gave a second injection a few hours later, as a final step, and then went on a lonely walk on Kendall Fell. When I came back she was dead. I was shattered by her loss, but felt that I had kept the pact that we had made and euthanasia had been entirely justified. The GP had been clear that she had only a few despairing weeks to live and I knew how deeply she was afraid of death. At the end I was considerably comforted by seeing her looking so peaceful.

Resuming commitments at the Hammersmith and preparing the Rock Carling monograph on communication in medicine eased the blow of

173

bereavement. On reaching April 1973 my thoughts were mainly on completing the monograph assignment. With the deadline closing-in I felt that I had left too little time in which to write a satisfactory 30,000 word text. And I struggled getting started. Deciding on the format proved difficult and with just eight weeks remaining I was close to panic. But I was rescued by the kindness of my latest Hammersmith chief, Chris Booth,[11] who knew of the problems and granted me leave of absence to concentrate on the project.

The first step was a decision to divide the book into two halves: the first on communication within various sectors of the health service and the second on communicating with the public on medical issues, with a major chapter on health education. While writing the chapter on doctor-patient communication I became shockingly aware of never having given thought to this aspect of medical care. Over a forty year medical career I had assumed that most doctors communicated effectively with patients, but a range of published assessments told a different story. Like the medical establishment, I had never given serious attention to a cardinal skill of medical practice. Acquiring communication skills was not a requirement of medical training. My campaigning for change began with the book I was writing.

I confess that under the stresses of writing *Communication in Medicine*[12] this anti-smoking campaigner took up pipe smoking again, which was a great help. This I abandoned, with due guilt, once the book was finished.

On the date of its publication by the Nuffield Provincial Hospitals Trust I gave the Rock-Carling Lecture introducing it. The interest generated by book and London lecture continued into meetings arranged by the NPHT to explore ways of promoting communication skills training in medical schools. But I never envisaged the extent to which I would be involved in this.

Maintaining links with chest physicians in the USA took me to New York, Williamsburg and a conference at Maryland in September 1973, after which I attended an

International Epidemiological Conference at Willemstad, Curacao, early in October.

During travels in America I learned of an impressive schools' curriculum project in Washington DC that innovatively instructed children aged between 9 and 11 on the workings of their bodies. I was so impressed by the health education value of this "Berkeley Project" [13] that, back in England, I strongly recommended that the Health Education Council consider undertaking a similar schools' project.

This was possibly my main contribution to the HEC, for in 1974, after visits to Washington by the Council's director of education, an immensely successful "My Body project" took off, beginning with a pilot study in Sheffield, which had a leading health education unit.[14] Of other contributions, my insistence on HEC promotions being based on established facts was also significant at a time when a first promotions director was more focused on impact than accuracy.

My Hammersmith Unit's controlled crossover trial comparing the effects of lower-nicotine/lower-tar cigarettes and conventional ones ended early in 1974. Health benefits had been difficult to detect in the twenty months of surveillance. There had been marginally less coughing recorded by subjects smoking the cigarettes with 30 per cent less tobacco, but no discernable changes in vital capacity or FEV_1 results. The timescale had been far too short. The main value of the trial had been in showing how comfortably heavy smokers (smoking more than 30 per day) had taken to the reduced tobacco cigarettes provided. Very few of the 160 who completed the trial had compensated by smoking more of them. Reducing the tobacco they smoked by 30 per cent had been acceptable. So although our short trial had not revealed health benefits, the cigarettes that we had trialled seemed a reasonable way of reducing tobacco consumption by smokers unable to give up, possibly with long-term advantages. Consequently, when reporting our findings in the *BMJ*,[15] we flag-labelled the need for much longer trials.

An encouraging development of 1974 was the Nuffield Provincial Hospital Trust's follow-up of my Rock Carling Lecture and monograph. I contributed to the two seminars that were arranged on doctor-patient communication. They brought together contributors from across medical and communication fields for exploratory discussion of how advances in communication skills might be achieved. We all benefited from hearing of pioneering initiatives by Peter Maguire,[16] a Manchester University psychologist, to improve the communication skills of local health care staff and medical students. Using video-recording of consultations and follow-up analysis, he had been showing doctors, nurses and students their communication inadequacies and ways of overcoming them. Maguire had taken an impressive lead in this field.

I contributed to a conference on smoking-related diseases at New York in June, 1974, then made brief view-sharing visits to colleagues in Philadelphia, Boston and Toronto.

This was the year in which my daughter Caroline married Christopher Clarke, a dedicated young lawyer.[17]

As the year concluded the results of Richard Peto's analysis of data from the 1961-1969 prospective study of chronic bronchitis provided the basis for a definitive text on the natural history of the disease and emphysema. With Richard, Cecily Tinker and Frank Speizer as co-authors, the compilation of this detailed work stretched far into 1975. Frank Speizer[18] had made important contributions to the project. Richard Peto had become the reader in cancer studies at Oxford University.

Among the delays in completing our monograph on chronic bronchitis was the time in which I was recovering from unexpected heart failure in May. This I experienced about a day after completing a strenuous DIY job at our Isle of Wight cottage. A few hours after returning to London I awoke in the middle of the night feeling ghastly, fearing that I would die. Still in fear I went to see the cardiologist at the Hammersmith who had diagnosed my angina back in the early 1960s. He found that I was in left heart failure, but without corresponding ECG evidence. He called it "the intermediate syndrome" and admitted me to the coronary care unit for several days. This episode kept me from attending the 3rd World Conference on Smoking and Health at New York at the beginning of June, and for several months I had a fairly disabling time with angina, which had troubled me only rarely in previous years.

My membership of the Health Education Council ended in 1975. This followed remarks that I made publicly at the press conference launch of the latest HEC anti-smoking initiative. I merely mentioned my disappointment at posters still being used when there was little evidence of their effectiveness, also that I had advised on poster effectiveness being researched before more were churned out. Harold Evans,[19] the HEC chairman, was very angry and at the luncheon afterwards condemned my undermining of the Council. So, I was not surprised that my membership of the HEC was not renewed a few months later when the time came for members to be reappointed. Only a few members of a Council of twenty were not, two of us critics of poster campaigning.[20] I had served for two four-year terms.

With 1976 I embarked on my last months as a National Health Service consultant, with retirement compulsory on reaching 65 in June. Before then I had the satisfaction of our detailed text on chronic bronchitis and emphysema being published; the culmination of two decades of research. Published by Oxford University Press, *The Natural History of Chronic Bronchitis and Emphysema*,[21] provided the clearest picture of chronic obstructive pulmonary disease yet available. A major chapter had been devoted to the development of chronic airflow obstruction and the principal causal influence of smoking. Of massive significance was recognition that many smokers do not run this risk. We drew attention to the value of detecting those who do within their early decades of smoking and advising against continuing. We saw excellent screening and advisory opportunities for GPs in a country where there were still around 24,000 deaths each year from chronic obstructive pulmonary disease and high levels of premature breathing disability.

From our lengthy prospective study we had been able to chart the slow decline in FEV_1 performance in non-smokers over decades, also the slightly higher rate of decline typical of susceptible smokers. Graphically we had been able to indicate the extent to which susceptible smokers were at risk of premature breathing difficulties, many before retirement age. But data for those who gave-up smoking emphasised the benefits. Within two years their rate of FEV_1 decline was approximately halved, followed by a steady return to normal in the next few years, reducing their risks of premature breathing difficulties and death from obstructive lung disease.

Also we were able to report the lack of a causal relationship between mucus hypersecretion and bronchial tract infection and the decline in FEV_1 in chronic bronchitis; contradicting our original hypothesis. In addition to publication of our monograph, findings of the 1960s prospective study were summarised in a paper to the *BMJ*.[22]

The final chapter in the story of chronic bronchitis remained for laboratory investigators to tell. A few years later they showed that long-term exposure of airways to tobacco smoke led to a sustained inflammatory response that reduced their diameter and could progress to the tissue damage of emphysema. Certain air pollution irritants were also found to be similarly inflammatory.

Retirement from the NHS in June 1976 brought a sudden end to my clinical and research career and I began rebalancing my life with other commitments and enjoying more time at the Isle of Wight cottage. But at home in London there were occasions when reduced commitments left me sinking into depression and needing adjustments to my medication.

1977 was considerably brightened by a new assignment. Aware that I had more time available, the secretary of the Nuffield Provincial Hospitals Trust,

Retired from the NHS, but ready for new challenges (c1976)

Gordon McLachlan,[23] commissioned me to visit all the country's medical schools and report on how much teaching of communication skills was going on and the methods used. Before further seminars on the subject, the Trust wanted a clear picture of the situation.

My first visits were to London medical schools, which proved devoid of communication skills training. I then went around the country recording a similar picture except at four or five universities, principally Birmingham, Manchester and Southampton, where there was teaching of real merit, mostly by professors of general practice and psychiatry.

My findings were reported at a NPHT seminar on doctor-patient communication in the autumn of 1977, at which it was decided that the deans of medical schools should be consulted on what steps the Trust could take to begin transforming the situation. John Walton,[24] the Newcastle neurologist who had become the chairman of the committee to lead further developments, took on the task of writing to medical school deans. In response to a series of questions they rejected the idea of conferences to stimulate interest, but approved the idea of articles in the *BMJ* and the *Lancet* on successful teaching methods. The most helpful response was from Oxford, where Peter Maguire had recently given an influential talk on doctor-patient communication. From there came the recommendation that the NPHT produce a short guidebook on achieving better communication with patients. This led to the popular, cartoon-illustrated "Little Blue Book": *Talking to Patients – Talking with Patients*, published a year later. Of a first edition print run of 1,500 copies, the NPHT sent 50 copies to each medical school and the rest were sold within a few months. After that, reprints were required to keep up with the growing demand from medical schools.

I took up the suggestion that short articles in the medical press could be used to increase awareness of the value of communication skills and over the next few months contributed a series of articles to the *BMJ*, providing introductory insights and guidelines. Initially, there was little response, but then requests for reprints began, eventually reaching a rate at which I could not keep-up with replies. Then later I heard that adaptations of the articles were being used in teaching at King's College, London, and as far away as Christchurch, New Zealand. The influence of the Nuffield Provincial Hospital Trust has slowly been spreading, but there is still a long way to go in ensuring that the teaching of communication skills is a basic part of medical education.

My College, the Royal College of Physicians, proved resistant to recommendations that communication skills should become an examined part of its membership examination, although I kept making them. I recommended that questions on communication be added to Part 2 of the MRCP examination, the clinical part in which patients are investigated, when it would be easy to test how much has been discovered of the patient's views of his illness and the kind of dialogue achieved. Slightly more complex, but worthwhile, would be to give each candidate a short case history to digest and then ask them to go into a television booth and tell the patient, an actor-patient, about his illness and what he/she needs to do about it. The candidate's video-recorded performance would then be assessed by an experienced lay-communicator, perhaps assisted by a clinical psychologist. Such tests would impress the need for clear speaking in words that patients can understand. My wartime colleague, Douglas Black,[25] when president of the College (from 1977-1983) did express hopes of such advances, but that was as far as it went.

Flying on Concorde is a major memory of 1978: a two-leg Air France flight from Paris to Brazil[26] where I attended a conference. Cruising supersonically at 1300 miles an hour shortened journey time considerably, but without Lou and me having the slightest impression of speed. This was to be my last long haul trip. Hypoglycaemic episodes in far away places had recently become more of a problem.[27]

Of considerable satisfaction in the later 1970s was the extent to which ASH, Action on Smoking and Health, became impressively political in campaigning, led by its first full-time director, Mike Daube,[28] a remarkable young force.

At last in 1979 *Your Life in Their Hands* returned to television screens with a younger presenter, Jonathan Miller, whose clinical and theatrical credentials made him an excellent choice. I had been considered too senior for the job. Now the programme had the benefits of colour that mine had missed. I appeared in one of them when a scheduled recorded programme had to be cancelled and a studio discussion programme took its place.[29] I sat on a panel that included health minister Gerard Vaughan and had the opportunity to attack his Conservative government's pathetic anti-smoking record.

As I moved into the 1980s, my professional commitments were largely in campaigning: campaigning for anti-smoking measures, for increased attention to communication skills in medicine, and for sensible debate on the legalising of euthanasia for a specially deserving minority. Also I would take up the challenge of creating a long-overdue patients' association for asthma sufferers.

Internationally, I travelled less. With increasing leisure I spent more time at our Isle of Wight holiday home where, with the help of local ornithologist Mrs Seabrook, my lifelong interest in birds has flourished. The cottage is a haven where we can enjoy produce from our garden and honey from hives that I have established. On fine days Lou and I go sailing, sometimes as far as the Needles, in our 16-foot clinker built dinghy, the *Queen Bee*. As I said to Lou when first we went there "I'm happy".

After I retired from the NHS and clinical work I sometimes became terribly down, but at the cottage depression is rare. Going there lifts me.

Coastguard Cottage and its view to the Solent

Chapter 10
Later years, still campaigning, final analysis

Anti-smoking campaigning continued strongly in the 1980s: as a leading spokesman of ASH of which I had become the president in 1979 and as a member of the Royal College of Physicians' committee on smoking and health, which published its fourth report in 1984. I had been involved in the compiling of all four reports. The fourth, *Health or Smoking?*, emphasised latest evidence that smoking accounted for the deaths of 100,000 British smokers annually. And for the first time we drew attention to the dangers of passive smoking, which were becoming clear. Finally, we urged the government to ban all advertising of tobacco products. Governments of the 1970s had resisted calls for a total ban and taken the safer political approach of negotiating voluntary agreements with the tobacco industry on advertising restrictions, agreements allowing the industry too many ways of continuing to promote its products. As the president of ASH I took every opportunity of denouncing the lack of a total ban.

But governments of the 1980s continued the voluntary agreement approach to tobacco company advertising, avoiding tougher confrontation with a powerful industry; an industry highly resourceful in avoiding a total ban, sometimes ruthlessly. In 1981, two 'ministers'[1] at the DHSS who favoured a total ban on tobacco advertising were transferred to other departments. On the grapevine we heard that this followed a tobacco company threat to withhold funding from the Conservative Party if they were not.[2] George Young went to the Department of the Environment and Patrick Jenkin to the Department of Industry. Earlier, in 1980, an attempt to discredit ASH at the highest level needed defusing. I had the job of advising the Secretary of State at the DHSS that we were not a subversive left wing organisation attacking smoking to damage a major private industry. On learning of the smear I invited Secretary of State Patrick Jenkin to dinner at my club, Brooks's, to meet senior ASH colleagues and set the record straight.

ASH celebrated ten years of campaigning in 1981 with a high profile conference. It had achieved forefront status in the growing anti-smoking movement through frequent press releases, a strongly influential information service to the press and all the publicity we could generate on the risks of smoking, plus numerous initiatives on smoking cessation, such as support for cessation clinics and the development of aid packs. We also led campaigning for smoke-free public buildings and workplaces in defence of the non-smoker and published guidelines for local authorities on smoking policy, plus no-smoking hotel guides. And considerable commitment went into lobbying politicians and leading opinion formers to assist political and public attitude changes against smoking.

Keith Ball, my successor as chairman of ASH, and its recently appointed director, Dr David Simpson, provided outstanding leadership in the 1980s. Although no longer involved in management decisions I continued following developments closely. Our main satisfaction was in the fall in numbers of smokers that consumer research was showing, although mainly within the professional classes. By the beginning of the 1980s Britain had more non-smokers than smokers. But data on women's smoking bucked the trend and was a concern that we strongly addressed.

Tribute is also due to other bodies at the forefront of 1980s anti-smoking campaigning, such as the Health Education Council and BMA, with which we collaborated. We also had support from the TUC. National No Smoking Day was introduced into the calendar in 1984, appropriately on Ash Wednesday. The increasing strength of the movement ensured increasing government measures against smoking, such as bolder health warnings on packaging and tax increases on cigarettes. But voluntary agreements on tobacco advertising continued, by which the industry retained a smaller but significant number of ways to continue promoting its products.

The 1980s were fulfilling years of campaigning and increasing leisure, particularly more frequent escapes to our Isle of Wight haven. And I had more time to spend with our nine grandchildren, although never matching Lou's wonderful caring patience. Mine is exhausted too quickly.

In 1983 we moved to live in West Square, London SW11, close to the Imperial War Museum. Moving home was a difficult decision and there were many stressful problems, but a West Square property had the advantage of providing ideal London accommodation (in a flat on the top floor) for our son-in-law, Nick Lyell, who had been an MP and PPS to the Attorney General since 1982. From the West Square address he could reach the voting lobbies at Westminster within the eight minutes of the division bell sounding. But for Lou and me it proved a stressful move with numerous problems and I required a major upgrade in medication to save me from deep depression. Becoming comfortably settled at West Square took more than a year.

In addition to 1980s anti-smoking campaigning, I went on contributing to the literature on doctor-patient communication and to the debate on euthanasia through the *Journal of Medical Ethics*, of which I had recently been a consultant editor (1976-1981). And various new interests in the welfare of asthma and diabetic patients had begun by the time we moved to West Square in 1983.

I had become a member of the Asthma Research Council in 1978, a body that since the 1930s had been committed exclusively to raising and allocating research funds, but my concerns were about standards of asthma treatment. Asthma deaths were still running at levels similar to previous decades, despite much better medication becoming available, and I thought that the

Council should be interested in problems of patient care. So early in the 1980s I suggested to Council that a committee be set up to promote better levels of treatment. I wanted GPs made much more aware of the needs of asthma patients. GPs were guilty of many of the mistakes leading to asthma deaths, often through not recognising when asthma was becoming dangerous. Too many asthmatics were left unaware that their asthma was getting worse. Also, I recommended strong guidelines being provided for hospital casualty (A & E) departments, where physicians were often dangerously lax in their treatment of asthma emergencies, many of them influenced by a traditional view that "asthma never kills anyone", which I had frequently encountered during medical training and witnessed how dangerous this could be.

The Asthma Research Council took on board my recommendations and a committee to promote greater attention to asthma patient care and emergency situations began its work in 1982, with me in the chair. Our first step was to design and distribute a poster of guidelines on emergency asthma care to all the country's casualty departments. The next was to promote the carrying of treatment advice cards by asthma patients in case of emergencies when they were travelling or on holiday. Away from home and exposed to different conditions the risks are often increased. The sample cards that we sent to GPs were designed to carry details of treatment needs, and we hoped that filling them in would reinforce GP awareness of the need to recognise severe episodes urgently and appropriate treatment. We began with a pilot study of GP responses. Some protested that we were trying to teach them their job, but most supported the initiative.

Unfortunately, a number of unexpected problems put the work of the committee on-hold after such a promising beginning, and not until the late-1980s did it take off again. A severe disagreement that I had with a leading committee member began the committee's difficulties. I arranged for a new chairman to take over, but soon afterwards the secretary moved on and then a highly supportive secretary of the Asthma Research Council died.[3] Impetus was then lost.

Also in the early 1980s I became involved in initiatives to improve the education of diabetic patients in self-care management. I had long been interested in advising diabetics on self-care, based on my own experiences. Back in the 1950s I recorded advice on a long-playing record produced for members of the Canadian Diabetic Association. Early in the 1980s I distilled my views on coping with diabetes into a RCP conference presentation[4] and a short paper to the *BMJ*, which had aroused lots of GP and patient interest and even resulted in a French version being published. But my interest was stretched to new levels by remarkable patient-education initiatives on the Isle of Wight by a locally based physician, Arun Banksi.[5] Initially he set out to improve the self-care education of the Island's diabetics by designing and arranging a short course for them, an event that had an inspiring outcome although not well attended. Only ten per cent of the population's five hundred diabetics took part, but when tested over half of them proved competent to serve as lay advisers to diabetics in their communities. Banksi followed this initiative with plans for a national conference on diabetic education for healthcare professionals. I was astounded that he planned to hold it on the Isle of Wight rather than on the mainland, but impressed when the event attracted about two hundred delegates, mainly health visitors and district nurses, plus representatives of the Diabetic Association. I assisted and John Butterfield came from Cambridge[6] to chair the event, which ended with a resounding resolution that an association of diabetic educators should be formed. This resulted in the Diabetic Association forming an education section, of which I became chairman.

To expand interest another conference followed and increasing numbers of health care professionals have become committed to better educating diabetics in self-care management. Follow-up has mainly been in assisting the development and promotion of video and computer-assisted learning programmes and audio-recordings of groups of diabetics in conversation with specialists.

Also in the mid-1980s I became involved in forming an asthma patients' association. In 1984 it dawned on me that asthma patients lacked such a support organisation and I wrote a short paper for the Asthma Research Council, of which I had been a member for six years, on the need for an Asthma Society. Sufferers of most other major diseases already had such societies representing their interests and providing valuable corporate support. There was agreement that such an association was overdue, but the way ahead proved difficult as the Research Council's constitution did not allow any departure from research commitments. A solution was eventually reached when the Friends of the Asthma Research Council, a fund-collecting support charity with a less rigid constitution, agreed that a patients' association could be launched as a constituent body organised by the Research Council. Nobly, the leaders of the charity allowed a massive modification of what they had established, virtually a take-over. And with generous financial support from Fisons, the producers of the asthma drug Intal, (sodium cromoglicate[7]) an impressive patients' association has developed under the charity's new name, the Asthma Society, which by the end of the 1980s had more than four times as many branches as the eighteen inherited from the Friends of the Asthma Research Council.

My main publications of the 1980s were on doctor-patient communication for the Nuffield Provincial Hospitals Trust, following in the wake of the Little Blue Books on talking with patients. In 1980 I edited the Trust's paperback volume *Talking with Patients – a teaching approach*. Then in 1987 I began working with Paul Freeling, the professor of general practice at St George's Hospital Medical School, on a sequel, *Talking and Listening to Patients*, published by the Trust in 1988. General practice was where the greatest progress had been made in doctor-patient communication, led by the Royal College of GPs.

In moving into the 1990s and my eighties I feel lucky to have survived so long after the heart attack of 1975. With more leisure and less to report the story is nearly complete. Until time runs out, my support for a range of health care charities and developments will continue. Increasingly, I value time spent at our Isle of Wight retreat with Lou, my loving ally of fifty years.

Looking back down sixty years in medicine I marvel at the unparalleled advances in health care and living standards that I have witnessed. The shocking poverty prevailing in the 1930s has largely gone, but not the overlarge differentials in income of the rich and poor, which I lament. My main political and social hope has been for a fairer distribution of wealth. I have always had an embarrassing impression of being overpaid.

But I have never been very political, except in backing socialist plans for a national health service in my early years in medicine, when I joined the Socialist Medical Association and voted Labour in support of them. And my clinical career has been almost exclusively as a National Health Service physician. In the 1950s I shifted to voting Liberal, feeling closer to traditional liberal values and the politics of many of my forebears. Now, I am modestly a liberal democrat. But however one votes, a fairer distribution of wealth still looks a far-distant prospect.

And the long-term future of the National Health Service looks highly vulnerable to steeply spiralling costs of high-tech medicine and advancing public demand. I fear for its survival. Without brilliant long-term planning, services will eventually degenerate. But in fear of electoral defeat leading politicians maintain the pretence of having the right solutions. I hope that when or before crisis-point is reached they will prove capable of bold rescue policies. Ideally, party-politics will be taken out of the equation and some all-party think-tank take charge of policy-making. The public will also need to play its part. Reducing the unnecessary use of services is strongly needed, also increasing regard for preventing the preventable. I am impressed by what the anti-smoking movement has achieved. It is very gratifying to go to a social event nowadays and find only about one in ten smoking. It was prevalent when we started campaigning and is increasingly the habit of a minority.

Among my major regrets is not becoming a professor of medicine in a London medical school. Teaching undergraduates was a considerable ambition. If I could live my life over again that is what I would concentrate on achieving. I would also wish to be free of the depression that has plagued me from the 1950s, although now fairly well controlled by medication. In company I usually feel effervescent, but when solitary soon sink into gloom, although rarely at our Isle of Wight cottage. Environment is a key factor. If I could have waved a magic wand to achieve one thing it would have been freedom from depression.

But life has had valued compensations. Advancing public knowledge of medicine as the country's first TV doctor was a wonderful challenge. Similarly, I feel fortunate in having led major research projects and national health promotion campaigns. And fate remarkably favoured me as the first doctor to witness the amazing therapeutic potential of penicillin, one of the great moments of medical history. On several occasions I have had the luck of being in the right place at the right time

Nearing the end of my story I do not have the comfort of religious belief. Occasionally, I drift into thinking of how wonderful it would be to be able to live one's life twice. Then I would have a second chance of becoming the professor of medicine I hoped to be.

**Charles Fletcher died on 15 December 1995,
four years after our last interview.**

Epilogue
Family reminiscences typified by the recollections of Mark Fletcher and Dr Veronica Lyell

Mark Fletcher: My earliest recollections of my father are of him working in the garden at our house in South Wales and of standing or sitting beside him while he worked and of his explaining to me as he did how the world and indeed the solar system worked. I have a memory of him telling me on one such occasion when I was only about six that the moon was cold and inert and that the light from it was simply reflected light from the sun. Until that moment I had not thought about the difference between the sun and the moon, they were just lights in the sky; but from then on I knew the difference.

Much later, when I was about 14, I remember telling my father of a school-friend's account of having seen a ghost. The account seemed convincing to me. But my father invited me to consider which was more likely: that all the well-established laws of physics had been suspended or that my friend had been mistaken in what he thought he had seen. He only had to ask that question for me to understand that my friend must have been mistaken. I still apply the "which is more likely" test to accounts of seemingly inexplicable stories.

In ways like this my father fostered in me an interest in the scientific explanation of how things work, which I have never lost.

My father was always distressed by people who made wrong decisions because they lacked a proper understanding of how things were. Later on, when the link between smoking and lung cancer became clear to doctors, I witnessed how determined he was to explain to the public and to governments that people were dying through ignorance of the link. I think that his determination to do something to publicise the link was driven by a moral conscience derived on his father's side from his non-conformist ancestors and on his mother's side from her strong religious conscience. (His Christian morality remained strong even though he lost his religious faith in his 20s.) He could not bear the thought that people were dying from ignorance. He raged at the immorality of the tobacco companies.

His desire to explain things also lay behind his belief that patients should be told about their health both in the doctor's surgery and by public communication through television and that this communication should be made using words that could be understood by patients and not in impenetrable jargon.

This desire to explain made him despair when he encountered views held (whether by other doctors or by politicians) without any supporting evidence or explanatory base. I remember his frequent complaints that politicians implemented policies without any attempt to ascertain whether the policies were likely to have the desired effect. He would be pleased to see the increasing recognition by governments nowadays of the need to have an evidence base for policy.

Veronica Lyell Byrne, my parents' oldest grandchild, followed him into a career in medicine and has written the following recollections from a grandchild's perspective. All his grandchildren have similar special memories.

Dr Veronica Lyell: I've loved reading these memoirs, which have completed for me so many partially understood pieces of my grandfather's life. They show his wide interests and deep contributions to medicine, and give context to the snippets I'd picked up from his anecdotes. He was such a huge figure in my childhood, and while growing up. I remember him in so many ways, especially practical ones, like his apple tree grafting and the preventing of windfalls by tying every apple stalk to its twig with black cotton. He was an inspiring mixture of handsome elitism and relaxed disregard for conventional roles, baking bread, knitting and making tapestry as contentedly as using his ever present Swiss army knife. His blood sugar meter was part of everyday life. I remember watching the bead of blood grow on his soil-lined fingerprint when we sat for lunch on the oak bench with blue cushions in the Isle of Wight garden, and then he would grunt at the reading, dial up the insulin pen, and roll up his trouser leg to inject his mealtime dose. I loved watching him in the kitchen at Coastguard Cottage, slicing the wax from the honey comb and setting it spinning in the machine, with honey gushing from the spout, like water from a clothes dryer. Sometimes a queen bee would arrive in the post in a matchbox. He told stories at mealtimes, telling his short Westmoreland anecdotes to make us laugh, and at picnic suppers on the beach the whole extended family would clamour for Hairy Rouky, an Irish fairy tale of lovely lilting repetitive phrases, which he said that his father had heard from his own father's friend. We had refrains to add at certain points in the story, and with the sound of waves on the sand, the crackling fire and three generations of voices joining-in they were magical evenings, once every summer.

His pleasure in explanation and clarity comes through in this biography, as it did in my childhood. I think he was always explaining things, with his expression quizzical and intent, and at one time I fancifully imagined I could learn medicine at his knee. Somehow he always seemed delighted by understanding. I remember seeing him in his hospital bed after he'd suffered his first stroke and had been delirious and unseeing for hours: he woke up and said 'Fascinating; a typical presentation of an occipital haemorrhage'.

We knew that he was important, but he also made it clear that he felt he could or should have been better, saying how he felt he was a 'regression to the mean' compared to his stellar father. I was vaguely aware of his depression, but his approach always seemed pragmatic; he was frank about all his medical problems and would say that 'If I find myself saying "Oh dear! Oh dear!" more than usual, then I know to increase my antidepressant dose'. His enquiring struggle with encroaching frailty in his last few years was fascinating. "Do you know, that there isn't yet a shred of evidence that physiotherapy actually works?" he told me as he carried out his exercises following a hip fracture. These recollections still assist me in practicing medicine for older people and help me understand how people's acceptance of limits adapts with time and circumstances.

But I feel very lucky to be able to remember him through his wonderful stories, jokes and magic tricks, his tap dancing and his powerful rowing stroke right into his old age, and I regard him and my grandmother as the ideal ageing couple, as well as taking a vicarious pride in his medical achievements as I am reminded of them in my daily work.

Notes

Chapter 1

1 See C Garwood in *Annals of Science*, 61 (2004) 99-117, for details of the career of Alfred Evans Fletcher (1827-1920) as a chief inspector of factories. He was one of two chief inspectors appointed in 1864 to enforce the 1863 Alkali Act, which sought major reductions in the output of noxious gases and chemical wastes by the vast sodium carbonate industry.

2 Samuel Morley,1809-86, woollen manufacturer, philanthropist (founder of Morley College), abolitionist and MP for Nottingham, 1865-66 and Bristol, 1868-85. His eldest son, Samuel, became Governor of the Bank of England.

3 Walter Morley Fletcher KBE CB MD ScD FRCP FRS, 1873-1933, double first in natural sciences, Cambridge 1894; medical degree, St Bartholomew's Hospital 1900, tutor and researcher in physiology at Cambridge, 1900-14, Secretary of the Medical Research Council, London, 1914-33. There is a biography by his wife Lady Maisie Fletcher: *The Bright Countenance*. London 1957. See also Munk's Roll of the Royal College of Physicians: Vol IV, 558-9.

4 Herbert Morley Fletcher, 1864-1950, MD, FRCP, Hon LLD. See biographical entry, RCP Munk's Roll, IV, 419-20.

5 James Cropper, 1823-1900, paper mill owner, 1845-1900, Liberal MP for Kendal 1880-1900. At the age of 22 after graduating from Edinburgh University, James Cropper purchased two paper mills, at Burneside and Cowan's Head, near Kendal, Westmorland (Cumbria) for £13,000. He had inherited sufficient capital from his grandfather. The mills had belonged to the Cowan Paper Company and originally been cotton mills. The story of the Croppers and their papermaking is told in Mark Cropper's *The Leaves We Write On*, London: 2004. See also T Jones and A H

197

Willink (1945) *James Cropper and Co Ltd and Memories of Burneside, 1845-1945*. Westmorland Gazette, Kendal.

6   Charles Cropper, 1852-1924, chairman, James Cropper and Co., 1880-1907 Senior Director, 1907-24, Director, London and North West Railways,1907-15, and exceptional horseman, huntsman and impressive water-colourist.

7   The house built by Walter Morley Fletcher, later a Hall of residence of Trinity College, Cambridge.

8   This was Steuart Wilson's first appearance in opera. In the late 1920s he became a leading performer of Elgar's Gerontius and recorded the work under Elgar. Later he became a music administrator as Director of Music, BBC, and later Deputy Administrator of the Royal Opera House, Covent Garden. He was knighted in 1948.

9   Alfred "Cony" Conybeare MA, 1878 -1952, distinguished Eton schoolmaster: housemaster 1909-30, Lower Master 1929-45, Vice-Provost 1945-52.

10 Montague Rhodes James OM MA, a leading medievalist and distinguished writer.

11 David McKenna, later chief commercial officer, British Railways, then general manager, Southern Region of BR, and from 1968-78 member of the British Railways Board; also chairman of governors, Sadler's Wells, 1962-76.

12 Bernard Fergusson, later British military officer, military historian, Governor-General of New Zealand and Baron Ballantrae.

13 Harry Cumming-Bruce, later British military officer and 7th Lord Thurlow.

14 Alan Hodgkin, OM KBE MA ScD FRS, Nobel laureate 1963. John Humphrey Plummer professor of biophysics, Cambridge, 1970-1981; Master of Trinity College, Cambridge, 1978-84; President of the Royal Society, 1970-1975.

Chapter 2

1   The Trinity College rowing club for Old Etonians and Old Westminsters.

2   Professor Joseph Barcroft, Kt CBE FRS, 1872-1947, professor of physiology at Cambridge, 1925-39; inventor of the Barcroft

differential blood gas manometer. His distinguished early investigations were of mammalian circulation. Later in his career he undertook studies of foetal physiology.

3   Dr Neville Willmer: a pioneer investigator of cell development in tissue culture.

4   Killerton, EX5 3LE: now a National Trust property and estate (6,400acres).

5   Francis Dyke Acland, 14th Baronet PC DL JP: Liberal Member of Parliament from 1906-39, Financial Secretary to the War Office, 1908-10, Under-secretary of State for Foreign Affairs, 1911-15, Financial Secretary to the Treasury, 1915.

6   W M Fletcher and C M Fletcher (1935) *The University Pitt Club, 1835-1935*. Cambridge University Press.

7   This rare form of pneumonia is now known to be due to infection by an Actinomycete: *A. meyeri*. Streptothrix was the name given to the infective organism until 1938, while it was wrongly regarded as a gram-positive anaerobic bacterium.

8   F R Winton and L E Bayliss (1927) *Human Physiology*. London.

9   One or two brief friendships with girls are later recalled, particularly a vacation spent at a house party in Aran, Scotland, in 1935, with the lovely Phyllis Gill, who became a friend in Fletcher's last year at Cambridge: "I drove to Scotland with Phyllis in a wonderful old Alvis that I had bought for five pounds. We motored right up to Gourock where we spent the night before taking the morning ferry. Although sexual advances were not on my mind and sex before marriage I had never contemplated, we needed to book into different hotels. It would have been quite improper for us to have done otherwise. In Aran we stayed at a house belonging to Alan Hodgkin's family. I was very attracted to Phyllis Gill and so was Alan Hodgkin, it turned out."

10 At that time the Cambridge Madrigal Society was brilliantly directed by its founder Boris Ord, the organist and choirmaster of King's College and one of the finest choirmasters of the 20th century.

11 A madrigal for six voices by John Wilbye, dating from 1609.

Chapter 3

1 The victim of the accident: Roddy Barclay, later Britain's ambassador in Brussels.
2 William Girling Ball FRCS, 1881-1945, Dean of St Bartholomew's Medical School, 1930-45.
3 Journeys to Bart's were by bus to Edgware Road Underground Station and then by rail on the Circle Line to Farringdon Street Station.
4 Harold Wilson, MS FRCS, 1880-1959, senior surgeon, St Bartholomew's Hospital, 1936-46. A fine general surgeon with special interests in urinary disease. Fletcher's first surgical placement was on the firm of Wilson and Geoffrey Keynes: the "Pink Firm".
5 Prontosil, developed in Germany, was introduced in the mid-1930s and proved effective against streptococcal diseases in humans. This pro-drug is metabolised into the antibiotic sulphanilamide.
6 MRCS LRCP: Member of the Royal College of Surgeons, Licentiate of the Royal College of Physicians.
7 Professor Thomas Renton Elliott CBE DSO MD FRCP FRS, 1877-1961, physician, University College Hospital, 1910-46. From early research at Cambridge he deduced the existence of chemical neurotransmission.
8 Basil Martin Wright, BM BCh, MA (later MD FRCP) 1912-2001, who was to become an internationally renowned inventor, particularly for his peak-flow meter and a very successful form of breathalyser.
9 First house appointment: 1 August-28 December, 1939.

Chapter 4

1 Howard George Bedford Russell, FRCS, Croix de Guerre, 1886-1957, (Australian born clinician, distinguished in World War 1) ENT specialist, St Bartholomew's Hospital, London, 1919-48.
2 Anne Fletcher had married the Reverend Stephan Hopkinson in 1933. Before marriage she had trained as an opera singer and

taken part in productions of the Sadler's Wells Opera Company.

3   Mrs Louisa Fletcher contributed a post-interview explanation of how she became a secretary in a secret service division of the Foreign Office: "I went because my father knew Sir Warren Fisher, who was head of the Treasury, who said that reliable young women with clerical skills were needed in MI6, as it is now called, and in addition to being a trained secretary I had the advantage of speaking French and German. Early in this appointment I was sent by administrative error to work in the highly classified document registry and was there for several months."

4   A salary based on what an Army lieutenant was paid.

5   C M Fletcher, Subacute Bacterial Endocarditis treated with Sulphapyridine and Heparin. *Lancet* 1940; 2: 512-14.

6   Dr George Graham, MD FRCP, 1882-1971; diabetes research, St Bartholomew's Hospital, London, 1920s, consultant physician, St Bartholomew's Hospital 1924-54.

7   Professor Leslie John Witts MD DSc FRCP, 1898-1982; professor of medicine, St Bartholomew's Hospital, London, 1934-38, first Nuffield professor of medicine, Oxford, 1938-65.

8   Lord Nuffield funded the creation of four clinical chairs in 1937.

9   Very few books had transferred to the New Bodleian Library by 1939.

10 Dr Alexander Macdougall Cooke DM FRCP, 1899-1999; consultant physician, Radcliffe Infirmary, Oxford, with specialist interests in diabetes, 1932-66.

11 Dr Leslie Cuthbert Cope, DM FRCP, 1903-75; Beit biochemistry research fellow, Oxford 1929-31, biochemistry research clinician, Rockefeller Hospital, New York, 1931-32, clinical research appointments in 1930s at St Thomas's Hospital and University College Hospital, London, then from 1938-42 at the Radcliffe Infirmary, Oxford, and ultimately at the Royal Postgraduate Medical School, Hammersmith, as reader in metabolic medicine. (Between 1942-46 he served as a Lt-Col in the RAMC.) In later years he became an international authority on adrenal steroids and published in 1972 the leading text on the subject.

12 Dr (later Sir) Douglas Kilgour Black, MD FRCP FRCPsych FRCOG FRACP, 1913-2002; MRC/Beit research fellow, Oxford 1939-42, professor of medicine, Manchester, 1959-73, Chief Scientist, Department of Health, 1973-77, President, Royal

College of Physicians, 1977-83, President, BMA, 1984-85.

13 Tingewick Society: named after the distinguished 13-14th century Oxford physician Nicholas de Tingewick, one time physician to King Edward 1 in 1302.

14 Professor (later Sir and Lord) Howard Walter Florey, OM, MD, FRCP, 1898-1968; Australian born physiologist, professor of pathology, Sheffield, 1931-35, professor of pathology and head of the Sir William Dunn School of Pathology, Oxford, 1935-62, President of the Royal Society, 1960-65; Nobel laureate, 1945.

15 Fletcher was unaware at this time that small samples of penicillin had been tested medically in Sheffield in 1930 and in New York in 1940. Cecil George Payne, a Sheffield pathologist, had used it successfully in treating a case of gonococcal infection in November 1930 and in treating several cases of eye infection. And in a New York Hospital in 1940 three patients with bacterial endocarditis had been injected with a crude extract of penicillin to test its antibacterial effectiveness against this infection. But Fletcher was the first to witness the revolutionary potential of penicillin.

16 Sir Ernst Boris Chain, DPhil HonFRCP FRS, 1906-79, German born biochemist, research at Cambridge 1933-35, at Oxford, 1935-46, later professor at the Institute of Health Rome and Imperial College, London; Nobel laureate, 1945.

17 The patient, John Cox (aged 4), a few days after appearing completely cured, died of a cerebral haemorrhage due to erosion of an artery wall by infection. But the post-mortem examination provided valuable confirmation that penicillin had completely cleared all infection.

18 Sir Edward Mellanby KCB GBE MD FRCP FRS, 1884-1955; Clinical physiologist 1913-33, appointed professor by the University of Sheffield in 1920 following his 1919 discovery of vitamin D and its part in the prevention of rickets, this post he left in 1933 to become Secretary of the Medical Research Council, in which post he remained until 1949.

19 Penicillin in this case was given by mouth with sufficient alkali to neutralize acid in the stomach.

20 EP Abraham, EB Chain, CM Fletcher, AD Gardner, NG Heatley, MA Jennings and HW Florey. *Lancet*, 2, 177 (1941).

21 Pencillin pioneers named in the Magdalen College Penicillin

Memorial Garden, Oxford: EP Abraham, EB Chain, CM Fletcher, HW Florey, MEH Florey, AD Gardner, NG Heatley, MA Jennings, J Orr-Ewing and AG Sanders.

22 BBC Panorama programme 7, 12 January, 1955: Sir Alexander Fleming interviewed by Dr Charles Fletcher (BBC Archive reference: LONGPROG, Catalogue Number 1187309/Film/Duration 0.11.38.

23 Gastroscopy: a diagnostic, endoscopic procedure for inspection of the upper part of the gastrointestinal tract (oesophagus and stomach) using a viewing gastroscope.

24 Solly Zuckerman OM KCB Kt MD DSc FRCP FRS, Lord Zuckerman of Burnham Thorpe, 1904-93, University lecturer in anatomy, Oxford, 1934-45, Government science adviser, Combined Operations HQ, 1939-46, Member of the Barlow Committee on Future UK Science Policy, 1946-48.

25 The Reverend Stephan Hopkinson MA, 1908-2004, vicar of Battersea, London, in World War II years, later vicar at St Mary Woolnoth in the City of London, then General Director of the Industrial Christian Fellowship and Anglican Adviser to Associated Television; Prebendary, St Paul's Cathedral from 1963. In the 1970s he became the resident Counsellor, Winchester College. (Brother of distinguished *Picture Post* editor, Sir Tom Hopkinson.)

26 Lady Mottistone: Evelyn "Evie" Izme Nicholson, 1886-1976, widow of George Crosfield Norris Nicholson and daughter of Montolio Oliphant-Murray, 1ˢᵗ Viscount Elibank; married Major General John Edward Seely, 1917.

27 Mottistone Manor, a 17ᵗʰ century manor house on the Isle of Wight, 8 miles south-west of Newport; home of the 1ˢᵗ and 2ⁿᵈ Lord Mottistone, bequeathed to the National Trust in 1965. (Post code: PO30 4EA)

28 Thomas Jeeves Horder, Lord Horder of Ashford, GCVO MD DCL FRCP, 1871-1955: physician-in-ordinary to Edward VII, George VI and Extra physician to Elizabeth II.

29 Major James ("Jem") Winstanley Cropper, 1879-1956, director of James Cropper and Co., paper manufacturers.

30 The Saturday, 25 October, 1941 edition of the *Hampshire Chronicle* carried a detailed account of the wedding. Bishop Cyril Garbett, soon the be the Archbishop of York in 1942, gave the blessing.

31 John Edward Bernard Seely: Major General Lord Mottistone CB CMG DSO PC TD (Croix de Guerre, Chevalier, Legion d'Honneur, Order of the Crown of Belgium) 1868-1947: Member of Parliament 1900-22; Secretary of State for War, 1912-14; Major General in command of Canadian Cavalry Brigade, World War I; Chairman of the National Savings Committee, 1926-43; Lord Lieutenant of Hampshire, 1918-47, created Baron Mottistone of Mottistone in the County of Southampton, 1933.

32 Details of this life-saving adventure are in Brough Scott's: *Galloper Jack. A Grandson's Search for a Forgotten Hero*, Macmillan, London, 2003.

33 J Seely, 1931, *Fear and be Slain. Adventures by Land, Sea and Air.* London, Hodder and Stoughton.

34 The heroics of this remarkable horse are also the subject of texts by Jack Seely and his grandson Brough Scott. See: J Seely, 1934, *My Horse Warrior.* Hodder and Stoughton, London; also J Seely and B Scott(ed.) 2011, *Warrior: the Amazing Story of a Real War Horse.* Racing Post Books, London; also B. Scott, 2012, *Galloper Jack: the Remarkable Story of the Man who Rode a Real War Horse.*

35 This November 1942 appointment was nominally as first assistant to Dr George Graham MD FRCP.

36 The Woolwich Memorial Hospital, Shooters Hill, Woolwich, London SE18, opened in 1928 as a memorial to troops from the area who had died in World War 1. In World War 2 it provided support for the nearby Royal Herbert RAMC Military Hospital.

37 Ronald Bodley Scott, later physician to King George VI and Queen Elizabeth II, and consultant to numerous hospitals and institutions; with specialist interests in haematology and chemotherapy; knighted in 1964, vice-president of the Royal College of Physicians, 1972.

38 Edward Revill Cullinan, later a leading consultant with specialist interests in gastroenterology and liver disease.

39 All Louisa's children were born in the occiput-posterior position, with head facing forwards instead of the normal backwards orientation.

40 Sir Francis Avery Jones CBE MD FCRP HonFRCS, 1910-98, research fellow, then first assistant, Medical Unit, St. Bartholomew's Hospital, London, 1936-38, casualty physician, St. Bartholomew's, 1939-40; consultant physician, Central Middlesex

Hospital, London, 1940-49; consulting physician, St Mark's Hospital for Colo-rectal Disorders, London, 1949-66. Founder member of the British Society of Gastroenterology, 1937.

41 Cuthbert Esquire Dukes OBE MD MSc FRCS FRCPath DPH, 1890-1977: hospital pathologist: St Mark's Hospital, London, 1922-29; St. Peter's Hospital, London, 1929-40; EMS Sector 3 hospitals, 1940-45; Hunterian Professor, Royal College of Surgeons, 1952; President of the Association of Clinical Pathologists, 1952; internationally renowned as the originator of systems of classification for prostate, bladder and colorectal cancers.

42 Dukes' Prognostic Colorectal Carcinoma Index, published in the mid-1930s.

43 Sir Francis Richard Fraser MD FRCP FRCPE, 1885-1964, assistant director, unit of clinical medicine, St Bartholomew's Hospital, 1920-22, then director and professor of medicine, 1922-34; director, new Postgraduate Medical School, Hammersmith, 1934-46; director, British Postgraduate Medical Federation, 1946-60.

44 Sir John McMichael MD FRCP FRCPE FRS, 1904-93, early research posts at University College Hospital (Beit Memorial Fellow), 1932-34; cardiovascular research, Edinburgh University, 1934-38, Reader in medicine, British Postgraduate Medical School (BPGMS) Hammersmith, London, 1938-40; acting-Director BPGMS, 1940-46; and director and professor, 1946-66: a leading clinical scientist of this era.

45 Lady Dorothy Meynell.

46 Dr Edward Peter Sharpey-Schafer FRCP, 1908-63, physician and medical scientist; professor of medicine, St Thomas's Hospital Medical School 1948-63.

47 In collaboration with Otto Edholm and Henry Barcroft of Queen's University, Belfast, McMichael and Sharpey-Shafer undertook for the MRC cardiac catherisation studies of haemorrhagic shock.

48 Dame Sheila Patricia Violet Sherlock DBE MD FRCP FRS, 1919-2002, distinguished physician and researcher of liver diseases. Professor of Medicine, Royal Free Hospital London, 1959-83, the first woman to hold a chair of medicine in Britain. In the mid-1940s she was an MRC fellow in McMichael's Hammersmith Department.

49 Pericardial effusion: an abnormal accumulation of fluid in the pericardial cavity sheathing the heart.

50 C M Fletcher, Cardiac Output in a Case of Pericardial Effusion: with a note on pericardial pain. *Br Heart J.* 1945, 7 (3):143-46.

51 Dr Philip Montague D'Arcy Hart CBE MD FRCP, 1900-2006, permanent member MRC research staff, 1936-48 (survey of miners' lung disease in S Wales 1937-39), Director MRC Tuberculosis Research Unit, 1948-65, then for 28 years a member of the National Institute of Medical Research.

52 Dr Richard Selwyn Francis Schilling CBE MD DSc FRCP FFCM DPH, 1911-97; medical inspector of factories 1939-42, Secretary, Industrial Health Research Board of the MRC 1942-46, reader in occupational health, Manchester, 1947-56, Professor of Occupational Health, London (LSHTM) 1960-76. His autobiography *A Challenging Life* (Canning Press, London,1998) includes comment on Fletcher's establishing of the MRC Pneumoconiosis Research Unit, S Wales, pp48-49.

53 Arthur Lewis Horner 1894-1968, son of a Welsh railway porter in a family of 16, became a dedicated member of the mining trade union movement in the 1920s, a member of the executive committee of the South Wales Miners' Federation in 1926 and its President from 1936-46, when he became General Secretary of the National Union of Mineworkers. A committed Communist for most of his adult life, he had political enemies and was jailed at Cardiff in 1932 on trumped up charges of being involved in "unlawful assembly".

Chapter 5

1 Report by P D Hart and E A Aslett: Privy Council, MRC (1942) *Chronic Pulmonary Disease in South Wales Coalminers.* Medical Studies Special Report Series 243. London: HMSO. See, also, details of MRC pneumoconiosis research in South Wales in the 1930s in recollections of P D Hart recorded in Volume 13 of the *Wellcome Witnesses to Twentieth Century Medicine* Series, 3-9.

2 Compensation in the form of a meagre pension or a modest pay-out of around £400, for which most miners opted.

3   McMichael had been involved in the assessment of respiratory disability in the first MRC survey of pneumoconiosis in South Wales.

4   Hickley Lodge was a fortunate purchase on which a reserve of £4,500 had been set at auction. The Fletcher bid was accepted by the owner at a time of fatal illness.

5   Alice Mary Stewart MD FRCP, 1906-2002, first assistant, Nuffield Department of Medicine, Oxford University, 1942-47 (seconded to the MRC Pneumoconiosis Research Unit, 1946-47); Reader in Social Medicine, Oxford University, 1953-74; Senior Research Fellow in Social Medicine, University of Birmingham, 1974-96; and honorary professor from 1996-2002. Biography: Gayle Green (1999) *The Woman Who Knew Too Much*. Ann Arbor, University of Michigan Press.

6   A personal letter of invitation to this meeting came from Sir Henry Dale, President of the Royal Society, who had been a friend of Sir Walter Morley Fletcher. The event was devoted to showing scientific advances of the wartime years. Attendance was in evening dress.

7   Later, the Institute of Aviation Medicine.

8   Arthur Landsborough Thomson Kt OBE DSc, 1890-1977, second secretary of the Medical Research Council, UK, and distinguished amateur ornithologist, author of *Half a Century of Medical Research*, Volumes 1 and 2. HMSO, 1973 and 1975, London.

9   Austin Bradford Hill Kt FRS, 1897-1991, epidemiologist and statistician, Reader in Vital Statistics, London School of Hygiene and Tropical Medicine (LSHTM), 1933, Professor of Medical Statistics, LSHTM, 1947. Hill pioneered randomised controlled trials in the late 1940s and early 1950s. He was president of the Royal Statistical Society from 1950-52.

10   Thermal precipitator: an instrument drawing air between two microscope slides, between which runs a heated wire to which dust particles respond by spreading themselves on the slides according to size across a thermal gradient. This is called thermal precipitation.

11   Philip Hugh-Jones, MD, FRCP, 1917-2010, physiologist, Pneumoconiosis Research Unit, 1946-51, member MRC Research

Unit, Jamaica, 1951-55, consultant in respiratory medicine, Hammersmith Postgraduate Medical School, London, 1955-76.

12 John Carey Gilson CBE, FRCP, FFOM, 1912-1989, physiologist, Pneumoconiosis Research Unit, 1946-1952, Director of the Unit 1952-1976.

13 Dr Philip Hugh-Jones recalled his appointment to the Pneumoconiosis Research Unit in 1946 in notes published in Volume 13 of the *Wellcome Witnesses to Twentieth Century Medicine* series, 31-33.

14 Several side rooms were eventually used for respiratory physiology.

15 Heinz Wolff, BSc FIBiol FIEE FIBES FRCP(Hon) FRSA, b1928, founder of the Brunel Institute for Bioengineering 1983 and professor of bioengineering, Brunel University, popular TV presenter of the 1980s and 1990s.

16 A recently introduced MRC award for technicians of special ability and of which Heinz Wolff was one of the first recipients. He lacked an O-level qualification in Latin and so could not go to either Oxford or Cambridge.

17 John Albert Penberthy Treasure BA PhD, 1924-2004, marketing director, J Walter Thompson Co Ltd 1960-67, director and vice chairman, 1967-74, director Rowntree Mackintosh plc, 1976-88, Dean and professor of marketing, City University Business School, London, 1978-82, chairman, History of AdvertisingTrust, 1985-91.

18 In the biography of Alice Stewart by Gayle Green (1999) *The Woman Who Knew Too Much: Alice Stewart and the Secrets of Radiation.* Ann Arbor, University of Michigan Press, it is wrongly stated that Alice Stewart set-up and directed the work of the Pneumoconiosis Research Unit (pp 59-60).

19 Jethro Gough, BSc MD FRCPath FRCP, 1903-79, lecturer then senior lecturer in pathology, Cardiff, 1929-48, and professor from 1948-69. Between 1940-50 he wrote a series of papers on coal workers' pneumoconiosis. The two disease hypothesis of pneumoconiosis and PMF was often referred to as the Gough hypothesis.

20 Peter Kerley, KCVO, CBE, MD, FFR, FRCP, FRCR, 1900-79, director of radiology, Westminster Hospital, London, 1950s and 1960s, Ministry of Health consultant on radiology, 1950-70, radiologist to the British Royal Family.

21 CM Fletcher, KJ Mann, I Davies *et al.*, "The Classification of

Radiographic Appearances in Coalminers' Pneumoconiosis".
Journal of the Faculty of Radiology, 1949, 1, 40-48.

22 "Notes on Indigestion, with simple dietary instructions." *The Practitioner*, January, 1949: reprinted as a pamphlet in 1950, 1954, 1955, 1956, 1958, 1959, 1963, 1964, 1966, 1968 and 1973.

23 Archibald Leman Cochrane CBE MD FRCP, 1909-88, member of the scientific staff of the Pneumoconiosis Research Unit, 1948-60, David Davies professor, Welsh National School of Medicine, 1960-69, honorary director, MRC epidemiology unit, Cardiff, 1960-74, first president of the UK Faculty of Community Medicine, 1972-74.

24 Richard Doll, Kt, CH, OBE, DM, DSc, FRCP, FRS, 1912-2005, member, MRC Statistical Unit, LSHTM, 1948-59, deputy director 1959-61, director 1961-69; lecturer in medical statistics and epidemiology, University College Hospital Medical School 1963-69, Regius professor of medicine, Oxford University 1969-79; first warden of Green College, Oxford, (later, Green Templeton College) 1979-83; discoverer of the link between smoking and lung cancer with Sir Austin Bradford Hill in 1952.

25 See Doll R and Hill AB (1952). The Study of the Aetiology of Carcinoma of the Lung. *Brit med J.* 2, 1271-86.

26 Jeremy Morris, CBE MD FRCP Hon FFCM 1910-2009) director, MRC Social Medicine Unit, London, 1948-75, professor of community health, University of London at the LSHTM, 1967-78.

27 The Haig Colliery, Whitehaven, Cumbria CA28 9BG, is now a mining museum.

28 A mine of the Millom Haematite and Iron Company.

29 John Craw FRCS Glasgow, orthopaedic surgeon, radiologist and medical officer of the Millom Haematite mine at Whitehaven.

30 Patrick Lawther CBE MD FRCP, 1921-2008, director, MRC Research Group on Atmospheric Pollution, 1956-66, honorary consultant in environmental medicine, St Bartholomew's Hospital London, 1962-81, professor of environmental and preventive medicine, 1968-1981. Lawther's research on atmospheric pollution and respiratory disease laid the groundwork for the UK Clean Air Acts of 1956 and 1968.

31 Owen Lyndon Wade CBE FRCP, 1921-2008, clinical assistant at the Pneumoconiosis Research Unit, Cardiff, 1948-51; senior

lecturer in medicine, University of Birmingham 1951-57, Professor of Therapeutics, Queen's University, Belfast, 1957-71, Professor of Therapeutics, University of Birmingham 1971-86.

32 Cochrane A, Davies I and Fletcher CM, "*Entente radiologique*: a step towards international agreement on the classification of radiographs in pneumoconiosis". *Brit J Ind Med.,* 1951, 8, 244-55.

33 International Labour Organisation Conference, Sydney, Australia, 28 February-11 March, 1950.

34 Max Leonard Rosenheim, KBE, CBE, FRCP, FRS, later Lord Camden, 1908-72; medical registrar, University College Hospital, 1936,1941, War service with RAMC, concluding as consultant physician to Land Forces, SE Asia, with rank of brigadier, consultant and deputy director of medical unit, UCH, 1946-51, professor of medicine and director of medical unit, UCH, 1951-70; president of the Royal College of Physicians, 1966-72.

35 *The Listener*, 28 September, 1950, 407.

36 C M Fletcher "Medical Research is Reducing Hazards of Mining". *The Municipal Journal*, 9 July 1949, 1811.

37 A Caplan (1953) "Certain Unusual Radiological Appearances in the Chest of Coal-miners Suffering from Rheumatoid Arthritis". *Thorax* 8 (1): 29-37.

38 John McGhie Rogan MD Edin, FRCP Edin, 1913-94, chief medical officer, National Coal Board, 1951-73. Before joining the NCB he had been a senior medical officer of the MRC.

39 Archie Cochrane CBE MD FRCP, 1909-89, became the David Davies professor of tuberculosis of Cardiff University and a renowned champion of randomised controlled trials. (See A Cochrane with M Blythe (1989) *One Man's Medicine. An Autobiography of Professor Archie Cochrane*. London, BMJ Books. (Now in a 2009 paperback edition by Cardiff University publications, also an Amazon Kindle edition.)

Chapter 6

1 John Guyett ("Guy") Scadding MD FRCP (1908-99): Dean and director of studies, London University Institute of Diseases of the Chest, 1947-62; consultant, the Brompton Hospital, 1937-72

and Hammersmith Hospital, London, 1946-72; professor of medicine, University of London, 1962-72. He is widely acknowledged as the leading respiratory physician of his generation.

2   The house: 3 Pembroke Villas, Richmond Green, Richmond-on-Thames, Surrey, had been listed for sale in *The Times*, about 3 months before the Fletchers return to the London area. Without delay, Lou had taken the train to London to purchase it, but had arrived too late. The property had been sold. But when the sale fell through about a week later her offer to purchase it was accepted.

3   Confirmed by Mrs Louisa Fletcher in an interview of March 1985.

4   Dr Erasmus Darwin Barlow, FRCPsych (1915-2005): senior lecturer in the medical school of St Thomas's Hospital , London, and honorary consultant to the Hospital, 1951-66, and member of the scientific staff of the MRC clinical Research Unit at University College Hospital. He was a great-grandson of Charles Darwin.

5   William Walters Sargant MA FRCP FRCPsych (1907-88): director of the department of psychological medicine and consultant, St Thomas's Hospital, London, 1948-72. An autobiography, *An Unquiet Mind*, published in 1967 by Heinemann, London, gives details of his own depression.

6   W Sargant and E Slater (1944) *An Introduction to Physical Methods of Treatment in Psychiatry.* London.

7   The party founded by Sir Richard Acland MP and J B Priestley in 1942.

8   Casualties of the great London smog exceeded 100,000 and there were more than 10,000 fatalities.

9   The Keppel Club, founded by Drs Jerry Morris and John Brotherston for an elite band of young physicians and medical administrators, met monthly at the London School of Hygiene and Tropical Medicine in Keppel Street, London, WC1E 7HT; hence the Club's name.

10 John Samuel Richardson, life peer from 1980, Bt Kt LVO MA MD FRCP, 1910-2004: consultant physician, St Thomas's Hospital, London, 1946-74, and at various times to the Metropolitan Police, the Army and the London Transport Board; physician to Harold Macmillan from 1952-70s; President of the BMA 1970-71 and of the General Medical Council, 1973-80.

11 J S Richardson, ed., (1955) *British Encyclopaedia of Medical Practice*. London, Butterworth and Co.

12 Donald Darnley Reid, MD PhD DSc FRCP, 1914-1977: lecturer in medical statistics, London School of Hygiene and Tropical Medicine 1946-50 (after wartime military service), reader in epidemiology (LSHTM) 1950-59, then professor in 1959 and director of the department of medical statistics and epidemiology 1961-76.

Chapter 7

1   Eric Frank Scowen Kt MD FRCP FRCS FRCPath 1910-2001, assistant director of the medical unit, Bart's, 1937-1955 and consultant general physician and reader in medicine, 1938-55, director of the renamed professorial medical unit, 1955-61, professor of medicine, 1961-75.

2   Peter Cardwell Elmes MD FRCP FFOM, 1921-2003, registrar, senior registrar and MRC research fellow, Hammersmith Postgraduate Medical School, 1952-58; lecturer, senior lecturer, reader, Queen's University, Belfast, 1958-1964; professor of therapeurics and pharmacology, Belfast, 1964-76; director, MRC Pneumoconiosis Research Unit, S Wales, 1976-85.

3   J Spence (c1950), "Phenomenology in Medicine". *Lancet*.

4   J G Scadding (1952) *Quarterly Journal of Medicine*, 21, 460.

5   In the late 1920s William Bosworth Castle discovered the "intrinsic factor" of gastric juice (now known to be a glycoprotein produced by the stomach's parietal cells) that is essential for the absorption of vitamin B12 and not produced by sufferers of pernicious anaemia. His discovery was a first step towards transforming their treatment.

6   William Alexander Briscoe DM FRCP FACP (1918-85) respiratory physician and physiologist, Bellevue Hospital and Columbia University, New York, 1956-69, professor of medicine, New York Hospital and Cornell Medical Centre, New York, 1968-73, co-author of *The Lung*, Chicago 1955.

7   Apart from the large fee from the California Medical Society, most lectures received fees of $100 – $200.

8   Lady Maisie Fletcher (1957) *The Bright Countenance*. London.

9   William John Hughes Butterfield Kt, OBE, DM,FRCP, later Lord Butterfield of Stetchford (1920-2000) member of MRC scientific staff (and Major RAMC 1947-50) 1946-58, professor of experimental medicine, Guy's Hospital, London, 1958-63, professor of medicine, Guy's, 1963-71, vice-chancellor, Nottingham University, 1971-75, Regius professor of physic, Cambridge University, 1976-87, vice-chancellor, Cambridge University, 1983-85.

10   Erasmus Barlow, a great-grandson of Charles Darwin.

11   A member of the Bach Choir from 1955-69 and member of the Organising Committee from 1958-1964.

12   Five series of *Your Life in Their Hands* were presented by Charles Fletcher between 1958 and 1964. Approximately 20 per cent of the viewing population viewed the programme.

13   The first reference to a causal link between smoking and chronic bronchitis was in a *Lancet* article of October 1955 by N C Oswald and V C Medvei.

14   George Godber GCB KCB MD FRCP DPH (1908-2009) deputy chief medical officer, Ministry of Health, 1950-60, chief medical officer MOH/DHSS, 1960-73.

15   Delegates at the CIBA Symposium at 41 Portland Place, London: EJM Campbell, JE Cotes, KW Donald, CM Fletcher, JC Gilson, AG Heppleston, P Hugh-Jones, G de J Lee, JG Leopold, CB McKerrow, RS McNeill, R Marshall, DD Reid, L McA Reid, JG Scadding, G Simon, T Simpson, CH Stuart Harris.

16   "Terminology, Definitions and Classification of Chronic Pulmonary Emphysema and Related Conditions. The Conclusions of a CIBA Conference." *Thorax*, 1959, 14, 286-299.

17   Robert Platt Kt MSc MD FRCP (1900-78): created Baron Platt of Grindleford in 1967: physician, Sheffield Royal Infirmary, 1931-41, LtCol. RAMC, 1941-44, professor of medicine, Manchester, 1946-67, president, Royal College of Physicians, 1957-62.

18   Members of the RCP Committee on Smoking and Atmospheric Pollution in Relation to Health : Sir Robert Platt (chairman), Sir Aubrey Lewis, Dr Guy Scadding, Dr Ronald Bodley Scott, Dr Francis Avery Jones, Dr Neville Oswald, Professor Jeremy Morris, Dr J A Scott and Dr Charles Fletcher (honorary secretary).

19 *Smoking and Health. A Report of the Royal College of Physicians on Smoking in Relation to Cancer of the Lung and Other Diseases*, published on 8 March, 1962.

20 *Your Life in Their Hands* had the highest viewing figures for a features programme.

21 Member of the Council of the Royal College of Physicians, 1959-62.

22 Appointed a WHO consultant on chronic bronchitis in 1962.

Chapter 8

1 The author is grateful for Dr Cecily M Tinker's recollections of the Unit's accommodation and employment of nurses, which have filled gaps in Professor Fletcher's recall.

2 Annual reports on smoking and health by the US Surgeon General's Department began in 1964: US Surgeon General's Advisory Committee on Smoking and Health (1964) *Smoking and Health*, Washington, US Public Health Service.

3 *Common Sense About Smoking* (1963), C M Fletcher's co-authors: economist Harvey Cole, who wrote on the economic effects of smoking, politician and journalist Lena Jeger, who discussed the social implications, and Dr Christopher Wood, who outlined ways of giving up smoking.

4 Respiratory Disease Experience Questionnaire: finalised and published by CM Fletcher and C Tinker.

5 Studies by Ferris revealed greater prevalence of cough, sputum production and chest colds in men with more than ten years exposure to vehicle exhaust fumes.

6 Research by Green and Cass at the Mallory Institute of Pathology, Boston. US-MA.

7 The manufacturers of Chesterfield Cigarettes: Liggett and Myers. For details of this long-running lawsuit, see R Kluger, 1997, *Ashes to Ashes*, Vintage Books, USA, 281-2, on *Pritchard v Liggett and Myers*.

8 Each sputum producing volunteer was supplied with three specimen tubes and a stamp-addressed envelope for returning sputum samples without delay to the Hammersmith Unit for next day investigation.

9   Ellergreen: the home of Lady Maisie's brother "Jem" Cropper.

10 Remuneration of c£500 per annum.

11 The London Medical Group, founded by the Rev Edward Shotter in 1963, was the forerunner of the Society for the Study of Medical Ethics and later the Institute of Medical Ethics.

12 Lord Robert Platt (chairman) and John Ellis (secretary) of the Association for the Study of Medical Education.

13 On the recommendation of the Cohen Committee on health education in England and Wales (1960-64) a new agency was needed at the centre of health education and the Health Education Council was formed to replace the Central Health Education Council that had led health education in England and Wales since 1927.

14 I Sutherland (1987) *Health Education – Half a Policy. The Rise and Fall of the Health Education Council.* National Extension College Trust, Cambridge.

15 In *Health Education – Half a Policy* (pp40-3) Sutherland has described the difficult relationship that developed between the chair of the HEC, Baroness Alma Birk, and the organisation's director general, Dr Bill Jones, also the problems that this compounded for the fledgling Health Education Council.

16 Dr John Stuart Cameron, later professor of renal medicine, Guy's Hospital Medical School.

17 Nicholas Lyell, who became the member of Parliament for Hemel Hempstead (1979-83) Mid-Bedfordshire (1983-97) NE Bedfordshire(1997-2001) and served as Solicitor General, 1987-92 and Attorney General 1992-7. (QC 1980, Kt 1987, PC 1990, Life Peer from 2005)

18 *Medicine Today*: monthly, late night programmes for GPs continuing from 1968-75.

19 Richard Peto, later professor of medical statistics and epidemiology at Oxford, FRS and Kt.

20 Members of the prospective study research team of 1961-69 not mentioned in the text:, Nurses: Helen Joyce (fieldwork team leader and initial coder and checker of survey data), Alison Sadler, Pat Orme, Mavis Williams, Elenore Spence, Julia Delgano, Alice and Loris Grote, Betty Jahn and Moira Stuart. Also the project had valuable assistance from nursing sisters Elliot and Cotton at the London Transport Workshops. Dr David L Miller participated in

the first two years of the study and developed sputum analysis techniques.

21 Sir David Jack CBE FRS, Research and Development Director, Allen and Hanburys, 1961-1978, Research and Development Director, Glaxo Pharmaceuticals, 1978-87.

22 The Society for the Study of Medical Ethics, founded in 1966.

Chapter 9

1 A grant from Secretary of State for Social Services Sir Keith Joseph with a warning to ASH not to expect further financial backing from the Ministry.

2 Dr Keith Ball FRCP, consultant cardiologist and founder of a department for heart and lung disease, Central Middlesex Hospital, and co-founder of ASH.

3 Dr Daniel Horn, non-medical US statistician, assistant director of statistical research, the American Cancer Society, 1947-57, senior official, US Public Health Service and Centers for Disease Control and major 1960s influence on US policies on smoking.

4 The first chair of the Health Education Council, Baroness Serota, resigned to take up a ministerial appointment in May 1968. Charles Fletcher took the chair until Baroness Birk was appointed in March 1969.

5 Visits to Hamilton and Stratford, Ontario.

6 Margaret Cropper (1885-1980), author and poet. Typical of her poetry is *Winter Peace:*

> *Where is the wind that raged and blew*
> *Til he made me fretful and harsh to you?*
> *We have another guest today.*
> *The shy sunlight that finds a way*
> *Into the heart of the room.*
> *December sunlight set around with gloom*
> *And precious beyond the summer's ray.*
> *It is so tender with hill and land.*
> *They do not remember how bare they stand,*
> *The trees content to bear no leaf.*
> *The field happy without a sheaf.*

Winter peace is so gentle a thing.
It eases the soul beyond anything
And makes a hope of the heart's grief.
Oh be patient and come and sit in this still sunlight
To savour it.
If the storm tricked our hearts with its fear
This shall shine in them, kind and clear.
I well remember another tone
Of hidden sweetness that we have known
And of things forgotten that once were dear.

(Published originally in the Westmorland Gazette)

7   A fellowship created a decade earlier by the Nuffield Provincial Hospitals Trust in memory of former Trustee and distinguished Westminster Hospital surgeon Sir Ernest Rock Carling. The 1972-73 Rock Carling Fellow received an honorarium of £900.

8   A L Cochrane (1972) *Effectiveness and Efficiency. Random Reflections on Health Services.* Nuffield Provincial Hospitals Trust, London.

9   Volunteers for the study were recruited by sending a simple questionnaire to all men in the 25-57 age range on the lists of six general practices in the Hammersmith area. Selected from the replies were men who smoked at least ten cigarettes a day, most of whom had a record of coughing. Trained fieldworkers then visited their homes and administered a more detailed questionnaire and measured their FEV1 and vital capacity performance, then advised them to stop smoking. From the ones who intended continuing smoking the final selection was made.

10 Omnipon, a synthesised morphine.

11 Professor (later Sir) Christopher Booth who succeeded Sir John McMichael as head of the Department of Medicine at the Royal Postgraduate Medical School Hammersmith in 1966.

12 C M Fletcher (1973) *Communication in Medicine.* Nuffield Provincial Hospitals Trust, London.

13 The Berkeley Project, begun in Washington DC in 1967, had three main teaching units: on heart, lungs and brain. The "My Body Project" in England was planned and introduced by the HEC Education Division, director Ian Sutherland. Details of the "My Body Project" are in I Sutherland (1987) *Health Education – Half a Policy.* National Extension College, Cambridge, 212-213.

14 The Sheffield City Health Education Unit, led by Area Health

Education Officer Frank StD Rowntree, MSc, founder of the Institute of Health Education.

15 Freedman S and Fletcher C M, *British Medical Journal*, 1976, 1, 1427-1430.

16 Peter Maguire (1939-2006) psychologist, lecturer in psychology then professor of psychological medicine, Manchester University, 1974-2004, and founder and director of the Cancer Research Campaign Psychological Medicine Research Group in 1988; a major international contributor to doctor-patient skills training and developer of the Maguire Model of communication training.

17 Christopher Simon Courtenay Stephenson Clarke, later QC (1985), High Court Judge (2005) and Lord Justice of Appeal (2013).

18 Dr Frank E Speizer: soon after this prospective study he became an assistant professor of Medicine in the Harvard Medical School, Boston, USA.

19 Sir Harold Evans, public relations specialist, Vickers Engineering; formerly public relations adviser to Prime Minister Harold Macmillan.

20 Critics of poster campaigning: C M Fletcher and paediatrician Richard Mayon-White.

21 C M Fletcher, R Peto, C Tinker and F Speizer (1976) *The Natural History of Chronic Bronchitis and Emphysema*. Oxford University Press, Oxford.

22 C M Fletcher and R Peto, The Natural History of Chronic Airflow Obstruction, *British Medical Journal*, 1977, 1, 1645-1648.

23 Gordon McLachlan CBE, Secretary of the Nuffield Provincial Hospitals Trust, 1940s-70s.

24 John Walton, later President of the General Medical Council, Warden of Green College, Oxford, and Lord Walton of Detchant.

25 Sir Douglas Black, President of the Royal College of Physicians, 1977-83, author of the Black Report on inequalities in health UK.

26 Scheduled Air France Concorde flight: Paris- Brazil, with a fuel stop at Dakar, Senegal, and destination Porto Alegre. Journey time: 3hrs Paris-Dakar; 3hrs 35 minutes Dakar-Porto Alegre. Subsonic return flights: Salvador-Lisbon, Lisbon-London.

27 Particularly a recent problem of not being woken by hypoglycaemic attacks.

28 Mike Daube: later director of public health policy, Western Australia, president of the Australian Council on Smoking and Health, professor of health policy and director of the Public Health Advocacy Institute, Curtin University, Perth, Australia.

29 This scheduled programme in the 1981 series was cancelled due to the death of a patient who appeared in it.

Chapter 10

1 George Young, Parliamentary Under-Secretary of State, DHSS, 1979-81; Patrick Jenkin, Secretary of State for Social Security, 1979-81.

2 From Department of Health sources ASH understood that tobacco industry pressure on the government was due to DHSS ministers' plans to ban tobacco product promotion by means of an amendment of the Medicines Act that would allow control of tobacco promotion without specific tobacco legislation.

3 Charles Fletcher's comment on this: *Then a tragedy happened. I had a slight fracas with one of the committee members and felt that it would be better to get someone in clinical practice to be the chairman of it. And I got Margaret Turner-Warwick, a professor at the Brompton Chest Institute to take over. And we got the Oxford consultant Donald Lane to be the secretary. But just as momentum was regained he became the acting secretary of the College (RCP) committee on smoking and health and had a lot of other things on. And then the Secretary of the Asthma Research Council died and the whole thing has gone into complete abeyance.*

4 Fletcher C M (1982). Avoiding diabetic disabilities without loss of freedom. *Journal of the Royal College of Physicians of London*, 16, 2, 78-9; (based on a paper read at an RCP Conference on Assessment and Management of Complex Disability in November 1981).

5 Arun Banksi: consultant physician on the Isle of Wight from 1978. Commemorating his work is the Arun Banksi Diabetes Centre, St Mary's Hospital, Isle of Wight; a recognised centre of excellence. Beginning in 1982, Banksi's Isle of Wight diabetes conferences became annual events.

219

6   John Butterfield, then Regius Professor of Physic and Vice-Chancellor of Cambridge University.

7   Sodium cromoglicate: the first clinically synthesised mast cell stabiliser, preventing the release of inflammatory mediators from mast cells.

Index

A

Aberdare Valley, S Wales 98, 102
Acland, Sir Francis 12
Acland, Sir Richard 116
Action on Smoking and Health
    (ASH) 167-169, 182, 185,
    186
Adams, Mary (BBC) 127
Adrian, Edgar 17
Agate, Dr John 114
Alexander, Albert 37-38
Alington, Dr Cyril 5
Alpers, Dr John 150
Angell, Dr James 33, 35
Akers, Elva 37
ASH (Action on Smoking and
    Health) 167-168, 169, 182,
    185, 186
Ashby, Professor Eric 104
Aslett, Dr Edward 61, 65, 66, 93
Association of Physicians of
    GB and Ireland 76, 139
Asthma, 1960s advances in med-
    ication 161-162
Asthma Research Council 185-
    188
Asthma Society 190
Atlas of pneumoconiosis radi-
    ographs 80

B

Bach Choir 135
Ball, Dr Keith 167, 168, 186
Ball, Dr William Girling 19, 30
Bank Hall Colliery, Burnley 93,
    111
Banksi, Dr Arun 189
Barcroft, Professor Joseph 11
Barlow, Dr Erasmus 115, 116,
    134
Bates, Dr David 96
BBC 101, 114, 115, 123, 126,
    127, 135, 136, 151, 157, 158
Beclomethasone 162
Bennet, Dr Edward A 116
Best, Professor Charles 100-101
Bevan, Aneurin 82-83
Black, Dr Douglas 32, 47, 181
Black, Dr Stephen 133
Blake, George 142
Blunt, Anthony 18
Booth, Sir Christopher 174
Briscoe, Professor Bill 129
British Medical Association 82,
    186
British Postgraduate Medical
    School, Hammersmith
    Hospital 55
Brocklebank, Tom 10
Brompton Hospital 113, 118
Brook, Dr Brian 51

Buchman, Frank 15
Burgess, Guy 18
Burrel's Field, Cambridge residence of Walter and Maisie Fletcher 2
Butterfield, Professor John 134, 158, 189

C

Cambridge University 9-18
Cameron, Dr John Stuart 158
Canadian Diabetic Association 101, 189
Caplan, Dr Anthony 103
Cardiac catheterisation 57
Castle, Professor Willie 129
Central Health Services Council 158
Central Middlesex Hospital 53, 58
Chain, Dr Ernst 38
Charles, Sir John 138
Christy, Professor Ronald 59, 95, 121, 123
CIBA Conference on chronic bronchitis and emphysema 138-139
Chronic bronchitis and emphysema 117-118, 120-121, 124-126, 135, 137-138, 139, 140-143, 145-146, 148, 149, 150, 153, 160-161, 176, 177-178
Churchill, Odette 114
Clarke, Bill 94
Clarke, Caroline 176
Clarke, Christopher (later Sir) 176

Classification of pneumoconiosis 80-81, 89, 108
Cochrane, Dr Archie 85-86, 91, 92, 93-94, 96-97, 101-103, 106, 120, 129, 171
Cohen, Dr Richard 20, 21
Colney Hatch Hospital, Friern Barnet 30, 49-55
Controlled crossover trial of reduced nicotine cigarettes 169, 175
Conybeare, Alfred 4
Cooke, Dr Alexander 32
Cope, Dr Cuthbert 32, 81
Council for Action on Smoking and Health (ASH) 167-168, 169, 182, 185, 186
Craw, Dr John 91
Crofton, Dr John 105, 114, 119
Cropper, Charles 2
Cropper, James 2
Cropper, James ('Jem') 2, 45
Cropper, Margaret 169
Cropper, Mary 'Maisie' 2
Cropper, Sybil 3
Cumming-Bruce, Harry 6
Cullinan, Dr Edward 50, 62

D

Daube, Mike 182
Davies, Alf (NUM) 90
Davies, Dr Idris 72, 73
Diabetic Association 189
Doll, Dr Richard 74, 85, 121, 160, 171
Dukes, Dr Cuthbert 54
Duncalf, Bill (BBC) 127, 135

E

Ellergreen family home of the Croppers 2, 6, 12, 33, 45, 84, 87, 152, 169

Elliott, Professor Thomas Renton 24-25, 99

Elmes, Dr Peter 125

Emergency Medical Service 27, 29, 55

Eton College 4-6, 21

Euthanasia 153-155, 156, 162, 173, 182, 187

Evans, Sir Harold 177

F

Fergusson, Bernard 6

Ferris, Dr Ben 148

Fleming, Sir Alexander 41, 123

Fletcher, Alfred 1

Fletcher, Anne 2, 6, 11, 17

Fletcher, Caroline 90, 107, 120, 134, 152, 156, 158, 172, 173, 176

Fletcher, Charles
    amateur dramatics 4, 15, 25-26, 29, 33-35,
    anti-smoking campaigning 138-140, 143, 146, 147, 167-169, 177, 182, 185-186
    BBC medical adviser 136, 151, 155, 157, 158
    birth 2
    Brackenbury scholarship 23
    Cambridge Blue 13, 18
    CBE 117
    carbon-copy diaries 49, 62-63
    chairman of ASH 168

choral singing 5, 9, 11, 18, 135

chronic bronchitis research 117-118, 124, 125-126, 137-138, 141, 142, 145, 148, 149, 150, 153, 160-161, 175, 177-178

clinical depression 115-117, 178, 182, 187, 192

'Communication in Medicine' 174

diabetes mellitus 33, 50, 97, 100, 141-142, 181

early education 3-4

electroconvulsive therapy (ECT) 116-117

Eton College 4-6

euthanasia, 153-155, 162, 173, 182, 187

house physician appointments 27-30

gastroscopy 43, 49, 53-54, 60, 61

Isle of Wight holiday cottage 146-147, 156, 158, 176, 178, 182, 183, 187, 191, 192

lecture tour of Australia and New Zealand, 1966 156

lecture tour, USA and Canada, 1957 127-130

London University reader in clinical epidemiology 145

marriage 45-47

MD thesis 60, 61

medical studies, Cambridge 9-15

medical training, London 19-24

'Medicine Today'
programme 157-158
member of the Oxford
Group 15, 17
member of the Central
Health Services Council
157-158
member of the Health
Education Council 158,
168, 175, 177, 186
Mother's death 173
MRCP examination 42-43
Nuffield research student,
Oxford 32, 36, 49
physiology research,
Cambridge 15-16
Penicillin, pilot clinical trials
35-41
pneumoconiosis research 61-
109
Professor of clinical epidemiology 172
retirement from NHS 178
Rock Carling fellowship 171,
172, 173-174,
rowing 9-13
Royal College of Physicians
Reports on Smoking and
Health 140, 143, 146,
167, 169, 185
tuberculosis patient 119-120
television presentations 114,
123, 126, 135-136, 151-
152, 153, 155
wartime appointments 27-60
wartime meetings with
Louisa Seely 31, 43-45
'Your Life in Their Hands'
127, 135-136, 143, 151,

155, 182
Fletcher, Caroline 90, 107, 119,
120, 132, 134, 152, 156, 158,
172, 173, 176
Fletcher, Dr Herbert Morley 1,
10.43, 60
Fletcher, Louisa 'Lou' 45-49, 51-
53, 56-57, 59, 66-67, 68, 84,
86, 87, 88, 89, 98, 104, 105,
106, 107, 114, 115, 116, 119,
120, 121, 127, 129, 134, 135,
151, 155, 156, 159, 173, 181,
182, 187, 191
Fletcher, Lady 'Maisie' 14-15, 25,
48-49, 52, 53, 62, 87, 130,
152, 169, 173
Fletcher, Mark 52, 54, 56, 67, 89,
107, 124, 134, 149, 152, 156,
158, 159, 193
Fletcher, Sarah 1
Fletcher, Susanna 56, 67, 89,
107, 119, 132, 134, 152, 156,
158,
Fletcher, Sir Walter Morley 1-3,
5, 9 10, 13-15
Florey, Professor Howard 35-41
Fraser, Sir Francis 55, 57
Freedman, Dr Stanley 168, 171,
172
Freeling, Professor Paul 190
Friends of the Asthma Research
Council 190

G
Gaitskell, Hugh 83
Garland, Dr Harry 100, 127-128
Gastroscopy 43, 49, 53-54, 60,
61
Gilson, Dr John 73, 74, 75, 90,

224

91, 95, 73, 74, 75, 90, 91, 92,
    95, 96, 99, 105, 118, 121, 135
Godber, Dr George 138, 139
Gough, Professor Jethro 78, 79,
Gough-Wentworth technique 78
Graham, Dr George 30, 50-51
    54, 55, 60
Grenfell Scheme 70
Grunbaum, Lionel 20, 22

H

Haig Colliery, Whitehaven 90-92
Hammersmith Hospital 55, 57-
    58, 60, 104, 113, 114, 117,
    118, 119, 121, 124, 133, 141,
    146, 148, 150, 151, 153-154,
    155, 157, 162, 174, 175
Harmer, Michael (MRCS) 63
Hart, Dr Philip D'Arcy 61, 65,
    66, 93
Health Education Council 158,
    168 175, 177, 186
Healy, Michael 171
Hewer, Dr Langton 22
Hill, Dr Charles 82
Hill, Dr David 145, 160
Hill, Professor Austin Bradford
    74, 81, 85, 145
Hill End Hospital, St Alban's 27-
    30
Hill, Robin 33
HM Prison Wormwood Scrubbs
    142
Hodgkin, Sir Alan 6, 16-17
Hopkins, Professor Frederick
    Gowland 2
Hopkinson, Rev Stephan 43, 59,
    87
Hopkinson, Anne 28, 87, 173

Horder, Sir Thomas 44
Horn, Dr Daniel 168, 169
Horner, Arthur 61
Hugh-Jones, Dr Philip 74, 76,
    95, 96, 105, 124, 134, 137,
    139
Hurst, Sir Arthur 54

I

International Epidemiological
    Association (IEA) 159, 169,
    175
International Labour
    Organisation (ILO) 99

J

Jack, Dr David 162
James, Montague Rhodes 5
Jarman, Dr Francis 102
Jenkin, Patrick 183, 184
Jenkins, Dr Thomas Harold 68
Jones, Andrew Miller (BBC) 114
Jones, Francis Avery 53, 58, 167
Jones, J.I.T. 69, 70
Joseph, Sir Keith 167, 169
'Journal of Medical Ethics' 187

K

Keppel Club 119
Kerley, Dr Peter 80
Killerton 12
Klein, Rudolph 172

L

Lawther, Dr Patrick 96
Leander Club 18, 137
Lewis, John Llewellyn (UMW)
    130
Lewis, Sir Aubrey 140

Llandough Hospital, Cardiff 67, 73, 75, 82, 83
London Medical Group 155-156
London Medical Students' Socialist Society 23
London School of Hygiene and Tropical Medicine 85, 119, 121, 125, 126, 151
London University 123-124
London Transport Engineering Works at Acton and Chiswick, 163, 164
Lyell, Nicholas 158, 187
Lyell, Dr Veronica 194-196
Lyell, Susanna 158

M
MacFarlane, Gwyn 47, 75
Maguire, Dr Peter 176, 180
Mann, Dr Karl 73
'Matters of Medicine' 114
Matthews, Bryan 16
McKenna, David 6, 9, 87,
McLachlan, Gordon 180
McLaughlin, James 148
McMichael, Professor John 56-60, 66, 99, 104-105, 113, 116, 117, 125, 135, 154
Medical Research Committee 2
Medical Research Council (MRC) 2, 24, 40, 58, 65, 66, 67, 68, 73, 74, 77, 78, 84, 104, 105, 106, 120-121, 140, 141
'Medicine Today' programme 158, 160
Mellanby, Sir Edward 24, 40, 58-59, 60 66, 73, 75, 84,
MI6 29
Miller, Dr Jonathan 182

Ministry of Fuel and Power 68, 69, 74
Ministry of Health 74, 138
Moral Rearmament Movement 15, 48
Morgan, Dr David 67, 83, 88
Morrell, Dr FH 72, 77, 78
Morris, Dr Jeremy 85, 140
Morse, David 20
Mottistone, Lady Evie 43, 48,
Mottistone, Major General Lord 28, 47-48
Mottistone Manor, home of the Seely family 28-29, 43, 84
MRC Committee on Chronic Bronchitis 120, 121, 123, 125
MRC Pneumoconiosis Research Unit, Cardiff 65-106

N
National Coal Board 81, 82, 90, 91, 92, 95, 98, 104, 105, 106
National Fitness Council 24
National Health Service 23, 82-83, 189
National No-Smoking Day 186
National Union of Mineworkers 61, 70, 90, 92, 98, 104
Natural history of pneumoconiosis hypotheses 77-78
Newhouse, Molly 47
Nicholson, John 28
Nuffield Provincial Hospitals Trust 171, 174, 176, 178, 180, 181, 190

O
Observer error 79, 80, 92, 127, 130

Oldham, Dr Peter 81, 94
Oswald, Dr Neville 140
Overholt, Dr Richard 148
Oxford Group 15, 17

P
Pallis, Dr Christopher 152
Paton, Alex 73
Peak Expiratory Flow Measurement 152-153
Peel, Mary 22
Penicillin 35-41, 123, 192
Peto, Richard 160, 161, 176,
Pierce, John 94
Pitt Club 12-13
Platt, Sir Robert 140
Pneumoconiosis research 65-109
Progressive massive fibrosis 65, 77-78, 79, 80, 81, 85, 96, 97, 101-103, 107, 108, 120
Prontosil 24
Prospective study of chronic bronchitis 140-141, 142-143, 145, 149, 150, 153, 160-161, 176, 177-178

Q
Queen's University, Belfast 104

R
Radcliffe Infirmary, Oxford 31-40, 75
Radiographic classification of pneumoconiosis and PMF 65, 81, 96, 97, 99, 106
'Random Collier Method' of dust sampling 94-95, 104
RCP Reports on smoking and health 140, 143, 146, 167, 169, 183
Reduced nicotine cigarettes 171-172, 175
Reid, Dr Donald 121, 125, 135,
Reid, Robert (BBC) 157
Rhondda Fach (Little Rhondda) 98, 101-103,
Richardson, Dr John 120, 121
Richmond-on-Thames 56, 105, 114, 115, 134, 156
Richmond Society 134
Roach, Stan 94
Robb-Smith, Dr Alastair 34
Rogers, Professor Harold 104
Rogan, Dr John 105
Rose, Dr Geoffrey 151
Rosenheim, Professor Max 99, 167, 168
Royal College of GPs 190
Royal College of Physicians 28, 31, 42, 140, 143, 160, 167, 169, 181, 185, 189
Royal Society of Medicine 147
Roughton, Francis 16
Russell, Dr Charles Scott 33-34
Russell, Dr Howard George Bedford 27-28
Ryle, Professor John 24

S
Salbutamol 161-162
Sargant, Dr William 115, 116, 117
Saunders, Dr Cicely 156
Scadding, Dr Guy 113, 118, 119, 126, 139, 140
Schilling, Dr Richard 61
Scott, Dr Ronald Bodley 50
Scowen, Dr Eric 123-124

Secret Intelligence Service (later MI6) 29, 49

Seely, Major General Jack, Lord Mottistone 28, 47-48

Seely, Louisa, later Mrs Charles Fletcher, 28-29, 31, 35, 43-45,

Sharpey-Shafer, Dr Peter 57, 60-61

Sherlock, Dr Sheila 58

Simpson, Dr David 186

Sir William Dunn School of Pathology, Oxford 36-38,

Smog (Great London Smog of 1952) 117, 121

Socialist Medical Association 191

Society for the Study of Medical Ethics 156

Speizer, Dr Frank 176

Spence, Sir James 125

St Bartholomew's Hospital, London 19-30, 49-55, 95, 123-124

Stefania and Paulo 90

Stewart, Dr Alice 70, 71, 73, 76, 77, 78, 86

Summerskill, Dr Edith 136

Sutherland, Ian 158

T

'Television Doctor' 151, 155

Third Trinity Boat Club 10

Thompson, Landsborough 73

Tingewick Society, Oxford 34-35

Tinker, Dr Cecily 141, 161, 176

Trade Union Congress 186

Treasure, John 76-77

Trinity College, Cambridge 1-2,

6, 10, 11, 13, 15, 16

Trinity Group 87

Two Valley's Scheme 97-98, 101-103, 120

Tylorstown Colliery 110

Tyntyla Hospital, Rhondda Fach 102

U

University Boat Race 1933 13, 18

University College Hospital, London 25, 99

University of London 123-124

US Surgeon General's Reports on Smoking and Health 146

US Union of Mine Workers (UMW) 130

V

Vaughan, Gerard 182

W

Wade, Dr Owen 96

Walton, Sir John 180

'Warrior', cavalry horse 48

Wartime blood transfusion Unit 31-32

Wattstown Colliery, Rhondda Fach 93

Welsh Regional Miniature Mass Radiography Service 98, 102,

Whitbread, Humphrey 87, 121

Wilmer, Neville 12

Wilson, Dr Max 138

Wilson, Harold FRCS 23, 63

Winton, Frank 16

Witts, Professor Leslie 30-33, 35-37, 43, 49, 53, 59, 70

228

Wolff, Heinz 75
Wolstenholme, Dr Gordon 135
Wooldridge, Dr Ian 134
Woolwich Memorial Hospital
    50, 53
World Health Organisation 143,
    168, 169
Wright, Dr Martin 25, 29, 51, 75,
    88, 96, 118, 152-153,

X
X-ray classification of pneumo-
    coniosis 81, 97, 99, 106, 108

Y
Young, Sir George 185
'Your Life in Their Hands' 127,
    135-136, 143, 151, 155, 182

Z
Zuckerman, Dr Solly 43